Bought
RHS Westn
H/13 A

A HANDBOOK OF NARCISSUS

A HANDBOOK OF
NARCISSUS

by

E. A. BOWLES

WATERSTONE · LONDON

First published in 1934.

This edition, with a new preface by Brian Mathew and
colour illustrations, published by Waterstone & Co. Limited in 1985
by kind permission of The Bodley Head Ltd.

The publishers are grateful to the
Harry Smith Horticultural Photographic Collection
for their kind permission to reproduce
the colour photographs in this book.

Cover Design by George Carter.

Printed and bound in Great Britain by
Richard Clay (The Chaucer Press) Ltd,
Bungay, Suffolk

Distributed (except in USA) by
Thames and Hudson Ltd.

ISBN 0 947752 55 2

PREFACE

CERTAIN books, because of their scholarly and historical content, never become outdated and are essential reference works for a particular subject. I regard E.A. Bowles's *Handbook of Narcissus* as one of the these. Written over fifty years ago it is, in places, a little out of touch with the modern developments in Daffodil hybrids, although it is surprising how many of the cultivars which one thinks of as being relatively modern, and which are so popular today, such as 'February Gold' and 'Silver Chimes', are mentioned, often with some interesting historical details of their origin.

Mention of history does I think highlight what this fascinating book is really about; for it holds a wealth of references and quotations from Narcissus literature, delving back as far as the sixteenth century and beyond, in order to gather together the often very astute observations of herbalists and botanists of old. And what an astonishing history this is, accentuated when brought together into one compact volume. Perhaps equally surprising is the paucity of new literature available today for one would expect, with such a popular group of plants, a proliferation of colourful books, such as have appeared on the subject of Lilies for example. The hope expressed by E.A. Bowles in the preface that his work would stimulate future writers has not really been fulfilled and there is as yet, no 'perfect book on Narcissus'.

On the practical side the *Handbook* is valuable in assisting those who wish to identify the wild species and varieties, with many interesting details of the distributions and habitats and how these have a bearing on their treatment in the garden. Bowles was of course primarily a great gardener so the chapter devoted to cultivation contains valuable advice which is as valid now as the day it was written. Although he was sad 'that a chapter with so disagreeable a heading' as *Pests and Diseases* had to be included, it is nevertheless well done and Bowles the Naturalist finds much more interesting things to say on the subject of the Large Narcissus Fly than merely how to despatch it!

Bowles is probably remembered more for his *Handbook of Crocus and Colchicum* than *The Narcissus* but this is of equal scholarship and literary quality and I am sure that the people for whom it was written, 'the garden-loving public', will continue to find great enjoyment in its pages.

BRIAN MATHEW

CONTENTS

LIST OF ILLUSTRATIONS

ILLUSTRATIONS

GLOSSARY

A GLOSSARY OF BOTANICAL TERMS AS USED FOR NARCISSUS

Alternate — Placed between other members of the same or of different whorls.

Anther — The upper portion of a stamen which contains the pollen.

Channel — A longitudinal groove in a leaf.

Corona — The cup, or trumpet-shaped or disc-like outgrowth, arising from the inner surface of the perianth at the bases of the segments.

Cylindric — Elongated, with a circular cross-section; compare junciform.

Emarginate — Having a concave notch cut out of the tip.

Filament — The stalk supporting an anther.

Filiform — Slender, rounded and thread-shaped.

Junciform — Slender, with a circular cross-section.

Limb — The expanded parts of a flower as distinct from the tube or throat.

Membranous — Thin and semi-transparent, used of the skin of tunic and spathe.

Neck — The upper narrowed portions of the bulb-scales— also used of the pedicel of the flower.

Opposite — Standing in front of, used of the leaves and parts of the flower.

Ovary — The immature seed vessel.

Pedicel — The slender portion of stem between base of spathe and ovary.

Perianth — The coloured floral leaves representing sepals and petals.

Perianth segment — One of the floral leaves of the perianth.

Perianth tube — The hollow cylindrical or funnel-shaped portion of the flower between the ovary and the segments.

Petals — The three floral leaves of the inner whorl of the perianth.

Petaloid	Of the substance or appearance of a petal.
Pistil	The female organ consisting of ovary, style and stigma.
Scape	A leafless flower stalk arising from the ground.
Scarious	Thin, dry and papery; not green.
Segments	The six divisions of the perianth arranged in an outer and inner series.
Sepals	The three floral leaves of the outer whorl of the perianth.
Sheathing leaf	One of a series of toughened, fleshy, tubular leaves enclosing the leaves and flowers until they reach the ground level.
Spathe	The semi-transparent, finally scarious, membranous envelope enclosing the young flower bud and the ovary.
Stamen	The male organ consisting of anther and filament.
Stigma	The upper part of the pistil which receives the pollen.
Style	The lower, slender part of the pistil which bears the stigma at its apex.
Throat	The funnel-shaped orifice of the flower where the perianth tube and perianth segments join.
Tube	See perianth tube.
Tunic	The membranous outer wrappings of the bulb.

ABBREVIATIONS

Bot. Mag.	.. ..	The Botanical Magazine, 1789-1934.
Bull.	.. ..	Bulletin.
Fig. ..	.. ..	Figure, an illustration.
fl. pl.	.. ..	Flore pleno, double-flowered.
Gard. Chron.	..	The Gardeners' Chronicle.
Lib. ..	.. ..	Book.
p. ..	.. ..	page.
Pl. ..	.. ..	Plate ⎫ a coloured illustration.
t. ..	.. ..	Tabula ⎭

Most of the illustrations referred to and the books quoted may be seen in the Lindley Library at the Royal Horticultural Society's Hall in Vincent Square, Westminster.

THE NARCISSUS

I

NAMES

NARCISSUS, Pliny states tersely to be 'a narce dictum, non a fabuloso puero'. Philemon Holland, in his fascinating translation made in 1601, enlarges this to 'for which narcoticke qualitie of stupifying and benumbing the senses, it took the name in Greek Narcissus, of Narce which betokeneth nummednesse or dulnesse of sense, and not of the young boy *Narcissus*, as the Poets do feign and fable'. Bauhin in the *Pinax* makes it to be from 'Narkosis', the condition occasioned by a narcotic.

Bulbocodium and Codiaminum are two names which crept into use in early times and seem to have originated from the blunders of copyists. Clusius and Caspar Bauhin attribute Bulbocodium to Theophrastus, but no such word occurs in any of the texts recognised as of first-class authority.

Clusius, writing of the names of Pseudo-Narcissus, states that Dodonæus named the common one N. sylvestris and that some think it is the βολβουκώδιον of Theophrastus, mentioned in his *Historia* among coronary plants which flower early, and that it is the Codiaminon of Pliny, which flowers twice. Theophrastus' list of flowers for garlands occurs in Book VI. viii. 1 (pp. 50 and 51 of Sir Arthur Hort's translation). After mentioning Narcissus and Anemone he places 'τὸ τοῦ βολβοῦ κώδνον', 'the head of purse tassels', which is Muscari comosum, and the two words bolbos and koduon seem to have been rolled into one as

13

bulbocodium in the texts used by those who, according to Clusius, connected it with N. sylvestris.   This was evidently so in the Greek text used by Gaza, for Bauhin in *Pinax*, Lib. II., sect. ii. 8, states that he translated Bulbocodium of Theophrastus as Codiaminum, following Pliny.

Theodore Gaza's translation, printed in 1483 at Treviso, was made from a manuscript that differed from any now known. Unfortunately, he did not confine his version to the MS. before him, but adopted many of Pliny's versions of Theophrastus.

Pliny's description of Codiaminum occurs in Lib. XXI., c. xi. It is described as flowering twice in the year, in Spring and in Autumn, and in the next sentence he writes that Narcissus flowers later.

Sir Arthur Hort has kindly looked into the history of these names for me and suggests that Codiaminum is a copyist's blunder for Cyclaminum. This would agree well with the two species of Cyclamen common in Italy, C. neapolitanum of Autumn and C. repandum of Spring. Many of the better MSS. of Pliny give Cicclaminum for Cyclaminum, and Schneider says older editions had Codiaminum. Gesner in Valerius Cordus' *Horti Germaniæ* (1561), p. 254, connected the name with the Greek kōdōn, a bell or trumpet, and stated that Codianum or Codiaminum with the flower of Codium was Campanula. The name Codium was also used for some kind of Lettuce.

Is it possible that Linnæus had the bell or mouth of a trumpet in mind when he selected this meaningless word Bulbocodium as a specific name for a Narcissus, a Crocus which has now become Romulea Bulbocodium, and as a generic name to include Bulbocodium vernum, nearly related to Colchicum, and B. serotinum, now Lloydia ?

In Nicholson's *Dictionary* Bulbocodium is stated to be derived ' from bolbos, a bulb, and kodion, wool, referring to the woolly covering of the bulbs'. Sir Arthur Hort tells me that koduon, a head, and not kodion, a diminutive of κῶας, kōas, a fleece, is the correct word in Theophrastus. Linnæus must have known that none of the plants for which he used the name have woolly coats.

Pseudo-Narcissus was first used for trumpet forms in Dodoens's *Hist. Plantarum* in 1557, and Lyte in his translation of 1578 used Bastarde Narcissus.

Tabernaemontanus' *Kräuterbuch* of 1613 makes it ' English Bastard Daffodil '. Clusius in his *Historia* (1601) uses it for Hoop Petticoats as well as Ajax (on p. 166). Gerard and the amending Johnson only use the English prefix ' bastard ' in the heading to their chapters on Trumpets, using Daffodil or Daffodilly for all, as in previous chapters for forms of poeticus, Tazetta and Jonquils. Parkinson loved a lengthy name, so never omitted bastard from his string of adjectives, as witnessed by ' the great double yellow Spanish bastard Daffodil '.

It should be remembered that no reference to hybridity was intended. In scientific nomenclature bastard was applied to things resembling, but not identical with, the species rightly bearing the name to which it was prefixed, generally with a sense of inferiority. Thus it was used of the lesser mouths of the Nile, a pale red as bastard-scarlet, and of many plants.

Laus tibi was used by Turner in 1548 in *The Names of Herbes*; ' Called of diverse, whyte Laus tibi, it maye be called also whyte Daffadyl.' Tusser also used this name in 1573.

Daffodil is a variant of Asphodel. In the fifteenth century the forms Affadille and Affodylle were in use. In 1538 Turner wrote (*Libellus* A. 3): ' Asphodelus a latinis *hasta regia* et *albucum* dicitur a barbaris et latine lingue corruptioribus *aphrodillus* et *affodillus*, et anglis *Affadyll* et *Daffadilly*.'

In Lyte's Dodoens of 1578 under Asphodel we read on p. 649: 'The flower is called in Greke *Asphodelus*, in Latine *Albucus*, in English also affodyl and Daffodyll,' while on p. 214 he wrote: 'Yellow Crowbels, Yellow Narcissus, Bastarde Narcissus, in French Coquelourde, and there is none other name to us yet knowen.'

However, Turner knew more and wrote in his *Herbal* of 1551: 'I could never see thys herbe (Asphodelos —ryght affodill) in England but ones, for the herbe that the people calleth here *affodill* or *daffodill* is a kynd of Narcissus.'

The *Oxford Dictionary* suggests that the confusion first arose through the use of the name Laus tibi for both Asphodel and Narcissus, and that after a time Affodil was applied to the former and Daffodil only to Narcissus.

In 1548 Turner wrote in *The Names of Herbes*, under Albucus: 'It may be named in Englishe whyte affodil, or Duche daffodil. This that we take for daffodil is a kinde of Narcissus.'

By 1597, the date of Gerard's *Herbal*, Daffodil was used for all kinds of Narcissus, and Parkinson in 1646 wrote: 'Many idle and ignorant Gardeners . . . doe call some of these Daffodills Narcissus, when as all know that know any Latine that Narcissus is the Latine name, and Daffodill the English of one and the same thing, and therefore alone without any other Epithite cannot properly distinguish severall things.'

In the third edition of the *Encyclopædia Britannica* (1797) we find 'the poetic daffodil or common white Narcissus'.

Modern popular prejudice tends to restrict Daffodil to yellow forms only, and especially to trumpets, in fact to the false or bastard Daffodils of those who first used the word. This may be because the Daffodil of Shakespeare, Herrick and the English poets generally is the Lent Lily, N. Pseudo-Narcissus, so widely spread as a native or naturalised plant. To English minds it represents the meads of Asphodel of foreign poets more nearly than any other plant which covers stretches of hillside, park and meadow with a carpet of bright flowers, yet pale enough to suggest a world of spirits.

The initial D has never been satisfactorily accounted for. It has been suggested that it may represent the final d of 'and', the Flemish article *de*, part of the definite article as a T softened down, or be due to a playful distortion, as in Ted for a shortened form of Edward, Nan from Ann, or Bob, where the repetition of a consonant makes a word more suitable for familiar use. A similar taste for alliteration may account for the extra d of Daffadowndilly.

Mrs. Lankester's statement, in Boswell Syme's *English Botany*, that Daffodil is 'the old English name affo dyle', which signified 'that which cometh early', and Dr. Prior's conjecture that Sapharoun-lily became Daffadown-dilly, lack sufficient historical evidence to be acceptable. In America the name Daffodil is mostly used for double forms.

Lyte, translating Dodoens, gives an interesting list of names including ' as witnesseth Dioscorides Leirion, bolbos emeticos, Bulbus vomitorius and Anydros ', in high Douch Narcissen Roszlin, and in base Almaigne Spaensche Jennettekens. Ferrari's *Cultura di Fiori*, printed at Rome in 1638, identifies N. vomitorius with Giunchiglia de Spagna. Pseudo-Narcissus is called Narcisso falso and Trombone; a minor form is Trombocino; and there are three forms of the Collo di Camelo, of which the single and double white seem to be N. poeticus and the pale single may be N. biflorus. Gerard wrote of this: ' The common white Daffodil with the yellow circle they call *Serin Cade*, that is to say, the King's chalice, and Dere bohini, Camel's neck, or as we do say of a thing with long spindle shinnes, long shankes, urging it from the long necke of the floure.' In Ferrari's Narciso non ha pari we recognise N. incomparabilis.

2

The French have used many popular names, the oldest of which is ' Porrion ', mentioned by Clusius in 1601, bestowed because the leaves resemble those of the Leek, Porrum. From Crispin de Pas in 1616, and Lyte's Dodoens, we have Coquelourde for Pseudo-Narcissus, while for recent names Coste's *Flore de France* gives Jaune Coucou, Trompette de Méduse for Bulbocodium, and for poeticus Jeannette blanche and Gant de Notre Dame. The spelling Jaunette is found in Tabernaemontanus. Saint-Hilaire's *Plantes de France* of 1822 gave fleur de Coucou and l'aiau.

For German names Matthioli supplies Vehtblumen, Hornungsblumen, February flower, and Zeitlosen. Tabernaemontanus adds to these Josephsstablein, all of them used for Pseudo-Narcissus, and Knorrs's *Thesaurus* of 1750 has ' vulgo Josephstefft '. C. de Pas gives Geel Tytloosen, spelt Tijdeloosen by Lyte, who adds Geel Sporckelbloemen and Spaensche Jennettekens. Modern German dictionaries give Affodillilie, gefüllte Narcisse and Narcisslilie.

Salisbury and Haworth named the greater number of the genera they created after Greek heroes or mythical characters. Thus Ajax, the tall hero in the Trojan War; Oileus, King of the Locrians, father of the lesser Ajax; Helena, the beautiful wife of Menelaus carried off by Paris; Hermione, daughter of Menelaus and Helena; Diomedes, fought against Troy; Ganymedes, cup-bearer of the Gods; Assaracus and Illus, his two brothers; and Tros, their father.

The strange-sounding name Queltia, given by Salisbury to the forms of N. incomparabilis, honours the memory of Nicholas Le Quelt, ' so famed in ancient story as a rhizotomist ' who discovered one form near Bagnères de Luchon. According to Lobel Le Quelt also discovered, in the mountains near Compostella, the plant Clusius figured as N. juncifolius, amplo calice, now recognised as N. odorus.

II

The Bulb

THE RESTING state of a Narcissus plant takes the form
of a tunicated bulb, that is to say, a specialised, under-
ground bud formed of a series of fleshy scales, most
of which completely enwrap the scale that is next
within. Thus, as in the familiar instance of a full-
grown Onion, an apparently solid bulb is formed by
the tightly-packed concentric coatings. They are
vase-shaped, narrow towards the base, of greatest
circumference at a third of their height, and narrowing
again upwards to form a neck. They are formed at
the bases of the leaves of previous seasons, which
become thick and fleshy to store reserves of food-
material, of which starch is the most important, and
also to retain a supply of the slimy juice found so
plentifully in the leaves and stalks of a growing
Narcissus.

The sap exudes freely from any cut portion of the
bulb scales, even in the case of a bulb kept out of the
ground for several months, and if smeared on a glass
slide and examined under a microscope it will be found
to contain a few grains of starch and a vast number of
needle-shaped, transparent crystals of calcium oxalate
called raphides.

These crystals, sharply pointed at both ends, are
responsible for the irritation of the skin known as
Lily rash among those who pick the flowers for market.
Some people are more liable to be affected by it than
others, but it is always dangerous to allow the juice
to get into a cut or abrasion of the skin. Smearing the
hands and wrists with tallow has been found a simple

and effective means of protection against Lily rash, but to wear rubber gloves provides still greater security.

Certain varieties of Narcissus are known to be more powerfully irritant than others. The Campernelle Jonquil and Narcissus poeticus ornatus are two of the worst, and some early-flowering Tazetta forms are nearly as bad.

So much can be learnt by cutting sections of a few bulbs that the murder of these innocents may be pardoned. It is best to select some of various sizes, that the differences may be noticed between double-nosed bulbs that have borne flowers in the previous one or more seasons; round single-nosed bulbs, in which the rings should be symmetrical throughout if they have not flowered; and offsets with one side flattened where it was pressed against the mother-bulb.

It is best to begin with the simplest form, a normal ' round ', and to examine it before making sections. At its base a flat corky plate represents a greatly condensed form of stem, similar to those usually found in true *bulbs*, as in Hyacinth, Onion and Lily. It should be compared with the greater development in bulk and for food storage seen in Crocus, Gladiolus, and on a larger scale still in Cyclamen, in all of which it is known as a *corm*.

In Narcissus and Lilium this abbreviated stem is more or less perennial, at least some part of it lasting for more than one season.

In vertical section it is seen to consist of two portions. The lower is the root-plate, with flattened base noticed from outside, from the upper and outer ring of which grow the roots of the current year. The upper portion cannot be readily parted from the lower, but has a rounded outline rising up into the heart of the bulb, and upon its summit the shoot of the coming year is seated.

In bulbs with side offsets still enclosed by some of the outer scales of the older bulb a separate centre with rounded outline can be distinguished for each offset. These solid layers represent the growth of three seasons, and the corky root-plate is an older portion of the one above it, pushed downwards by the succeeding year's growth.

The upper and whiter portions are closely analogous to the annually formed corm of a Crocus. Both root-plate and corm-like body emit starch granules freely when thinly sliced and placed in water.

A dry bulb examined in August or September should be completely covered with thin tunics of semi-transparent, brown membrane. These are formed of the bases of leaves of previous seasons from which the starch and raphides have been absorbed, and only the inner and outer skins remain and are fused into one.

Several of these outer coats may be ragged through partial decay, and so loosely attached that they can be removed by a slight rubbing until none but closely-fitting skins are left.

These are semi-transparent, of many shades of brown from that of raw sienna, through burnt sienna to sepia, and marked with darker, parallel veins from base to tip.

The most pleasing tunics, both in their close fit and shining, satin-like texture, are to be found in bulbs of Jonquils and Tazettas; the coarsest and dullest occur in some trumpet and poeticus forms.

The outermost coats are joined to the bulb at their bases just above the basal root-plate and seldom reach further upward than the point of widest circumference, where the upper portion of the tunic next within carries on the investment, which proceeds in a similar succession of scale tips to the top of the narrow neck, where, in some instances, the cavity is closed by the

dry, flattened tip of the remains of the last season's
scape as neatly as a cork fits into a bottle.

If the upper edges of these dry tunics are prised
away from the bulb it will be seen that the scarious,
dried portion generally extends for only a short distance below the upper edge of the outer scale that
overlaps it, and that the lower portion of these scales
is fleshy and white, and is still performing the work of
storage; also that the scarious tip becomes shorter
and the fleshy portion longer in each inwardly succeeding scale.

Another point worth noticing is that as the upper
portion of a scale dries up it sometimes shrinks unevenly, and a prominent ridge or wrinkle is formed
which in some cases looks as though it were a node,
but as nothing of the kind can be found in such scales
while still in the fleshy condition, it is clearly only the
result of shrinkage. As similar ridges occasionally
appear in withered scapes, we may find here the explanation of the puzzling node-like construction seen
in the specimen of N. serotinus in Linnæus's herbarium.

On carefully removing one of these scales with
scarious tips, by slitting it up on one side and cutting
it from off the root-plate, it may be observed that there
is a thin, almost transparent membrane on its inner
surface, joined to the thicker, fleshy or spongy tissue
of the outer layer right at its base, and again where the
two surfaces become fused together at the top to form
the scarious tunic.

This membrane is devoid of the parallel veins to
be seen in the fleshy outer portion, and frequently
adheres so closely to the polished outer surface of the
scale next within as to appear to belong to it as an
outer skin. That it is actually the inner lining of the
fleshy portion is shown by two facts: first that axillary
buds which grow into offsets are formed between this

shining membrane and the outer surface of the scale next towards the centre of the bulb, and secondly that when the membrane and fleshy portion have not fused uniformly in becoming scarious, the thinner portion in some cases forms a small blister or stands out alone at the upper edge, but always on the inner surface in both instances.

A bulb cut transversely through the point of greatest circumference pours out so much viscous sap from the sections that at first they are difficult and unpleasant to examine. Thinner sections of $\frac{1}{4}$ to $\frac{1}{2}$ inch thick should be cut, and all four parts laid aside for an hour or two that the sap may dry and the scales shrink a little and so be easier to observe. Commencing from the outside, the rings are generally of nearly uniform thickness, concentric and so closely pressed against each other that sometimes it is difficult to count their number without inserting a dissecting needle between the layers. There may be from two to five of them, and they are formed from the bases of the sheathing leaves of the previous season or the one before that.

They are followed, counting towards the centre of the bulb, by two or more completely enwrapping circular scales, each of which is considerably thicker on one side, and the thick side of one is contiguous to the thin side of the next. The substance of the thickened side is sometimes spongy and occasionally somewhat corrugated, in which case an air space exists between the two scales.

Such scales of uneven thickness are those formed from the outermost true leaves of a previous season's growth. Proof of this may be found by examining the bases of the leaves at flowering time or later. It will be seen that the outer two, three or four, though flat in their upper portions, become tubular at their bases, thickening alternately on opposite sides, and that the thicker side of this tubular portion is always that from which the blade of the leaf arises.

If the bulb under examination flowered in the season when these scales were formed there will be found two scales of different conformations. First, one that only extends for about half of the circumference of the bulb. It closely resembles the scale outside it in texture, and is thicker in its central portion than at its ends, both of which are doubled back on itself inwardly, thus only enwrapping the outer side of the next inner organ. This is a curved, scale-like body formed of a circular skin that has been compressed so that the two sides meet closely at its centre, but generally terminate with a space between them, forming a loop at either end. It is the base of the flowering scape, the lower portion of which stores food-supplies similarly to the leaf bases.

The scale with doubled-in ends is formed from the leaf next to the scape on its outer side, which, instead of becoming tubular at its base, has its edges bent inward for a little way to enclose the keeled edges of the scape. This leaf is called the subtending leaf and represents a bract, in the axil of which the flower bud is produced. It is faced on the other side of the scape by a leaf in whose axil the bud for the following season's growth is formed, and which has a tubular base enclosing the subtending leaf and scape as well as the growth bud.

Even in early Autumn, and at any time while the bulb is in active growth, it is easy to continue the investigation and to recognise in the young growth the cylindrical scales of uniform thickness at the bases of sheathing leaves, the scales at the bases of leaves with one side thickened, and the subtending leaf's semicylindrical scale next to the scape and its opposite leaf beyond the growth bud.

I have found old bulbs in which twenty-four succes-

sive scales were counted, and in which two old scapes,
and one for the following Spring, were present. These,
with the addition of the embryonic growth bud, represent five seasons thus:

For 1931   3 layers of scarious skins.
For 1932   2 thin rings=sheathing leaves.
           2 thickened=leaves.
           1 half ring=subtending leaf.
           1 scape   No. 1.
For 1933   2 thin
           2 thickened
           1 half
           1 scape   No. 2.
For 1934   3 thin
           4 leaves
           1 scape   No. 3.
For 1935   the growth bud.

Offsets commence life in the axils of leaves or scales
other than that enclosing the central shoot. They are
gradually pushed to the side of the mother-bulb by
the growth of the main central shoot. The annual
conversion of outer scales into membranous coats and
their final decay and disappearance eventually permit
the offsets to come into contact with the soil. They
are then still attached on their inner sides to the main
bulb, but only at the root base.

Under cultivation it is generally advisable to remove
offsets when no longer enclosed by the membrane
of the mother-bulb and when the attachment is only
by a small portion of the root base. So long as an
offset is still attached only those roots that spring from
the free outer side of its root base can function
properly.

When more than one offset is formed they appear
on opposite sides of the mother-bulb. This results
from the distichous phyllotaxy of Narcissus—that is

to say the leaves, and the scales into which they afterwards develop, are arranged in opposite ranks of one
and one—and accounts for the crowding of offsets one
below another on opposite sides of bulbs that have
been left too long without lifting and dividing.

It is interesting to observe that the leaves of offsets
are arranged in the same plane as those of their parent.

III

THE FLOWER AND LEAF

IN THE genus Narcissus the flower is mainly formed on the general lines of the Natural Order Amaryllideæ.

Thus the ovary is *inferior* to the perianth, which is to say the seedpod is below and outside the coloured portions that in everyday language are called the flower. In this Amaryllids resemble Irids, but differ from Liliaceous plants in which the ovary is *superior*, placed above and within the position where the perianth segments, or the tube that carries them, are joined to the stalk. Narcissus, however, differs from all but its nearest allies in possessing a remarkable secondary growth, which looks like an extra corolla or floral whorl, arising from the bases of the perianth segments and known as the *corona*.

Describing the flower from below upwards we find the stalk, or stem, which should be called a *scape* because it is ' a leafless floral axis or peduncle arising from the ground '.

It is made up of two portions (internodes), first the thicker, longer, lower part, the *peduncle*, which we speak of as the stem; at the top of this there is a joint, or node, where the spathe is found and the *pedicel* commences. This is the upper, more slender continuation of the scape, sometimes called the neck. It varies greatly as to length in different forms, and as it grows unevenly on its upper and lower sides while young it becomes curved and causes the flower to stand away from the scape at various angles from nearly upright, through a horizontal position to one almost as pendent as that of a Fuchsia.

The peduncle varies from cylindrical and smooth, as

in N. viridiflorus, Jonquilla and others, to flattened and strongly ribbed, as in Tazetta and the greater number of other species.

It is generally strongly keeled at its two edges, with a number of lesser ribs between these two keels, which are frequently so prominent that a blind man could detect them by touch.

This flattened form results from, or at any rate fits in with, the lateral compression met with in the scape's early stages, between the ranks of leaves that stand on either side of it in the heart of the bulb.

It should be noticed that the flattening is absent in those species that produce no leaf in the same season as a scape, such as N. viridiflorus and serotinus, and is least noticeable in those like Jonquilla, whose narrow leaves are slightly flattened on the surface that is pressed against the scape.

The keels are continued upwards above the node to form the strongest ribs, or even keels, of the *spathe*, the tubular sheathing skin that encloses and protects the flower bud in its young stages. This interesting organ is peculiar in several ways. It commences as two separate, minute outgrowths which arise at a very early stage of the development of the flowers on opposite sides of the scape in a *transverse* plane to that of the true leaves. This is necessary, because these prophylls (forerunners of leafy members) spring from the keels, the strength-giving, ribbed edges of the scape, which occupy the spaces between the margins of the embryonic leaves.

At an early stage these two prophylls fuse and form a closed sheath around the floral organs, but occasionally at maturity they still bear two small lobes at the tip showing the nature of their origin, which is also witnessed to by their keels. They may be compared with the spathes of Galanthus, in which these characters are more obvious.

The pressure from within of the maturing flower bud causes the membrane of the spathe to split in its upper portion on the lower side, liberating the closed flower. At this stage the membrane generally dries and wrinkles back, but remains tubular below, where it still enwraps the pedicel and ovary.

The whole structure is a very elaborate organ designed to perform a special protective function for the young flower and seedpod.

The *ovary*, or seedpod, is botanically described as being in the receptacle, trilocular, with two rows of seeds in each loculus, and twelve seeds in a row.

The green wall of the ovary is continued at its summit to form the tube from which the perianth segments, and generally the stamens, are produced.

This tube is very short in N. cyclamineus, long and cylindrical in N. poeticus, Jonquilla and Tazetta, and varying in length and width, but for the most part funnel-shaped, in trumpet forms and their derivatives.

The *nectaries* (honey glands) are found at the base of this tube, consisting of three pocket-like glands sunk in the partitions that divide the three chambers (loculi) of the ovary. In these the honey is secreted and is poured out to lie at the bottom of the tube in wide-tubed forms, but rises higher within grooves between internal ridges in the long, narrow tube of N. poeticus and similarly constructed flowers.

The *stamens* are six in number and vary greatly as to the length of the *filaments*, the slender, stalk-like portions that support the *anthers*, the sac-like bodies containing the pollen. The filaments spring from the base of the tube in the Ajax (trumpet) species and N. Bulbocodium. In the last they are curved downwards at their bases so that they lie against the lower portion of the long tube for about half its length and then curve upwards at a different point in the length of each, so that the anthers are held up apart from one another. In all other species and forms the filaments are straight, and except in the small N. asturiensis (minimus of gardens) they are joined to the tube in two alternate ranks of longer and shorter filaments.

In Ajax they are long and inserted almost at the base of the tube. The other extreme is reached in N. poeticus and Tazetta, where the lower three spring out from but little below the throat to halfway down the tube and the upper set from the mouth, and in both ranks they are so short that the anthers appear almost sessile.

The *pistil* consists of three parts, the *style*, which is the long slender column that bears at its top a small, three-lobed expansion which is the *stigma*, the organ specialised for the reception of pollen for the fertilisation of the embryonic seeds (ovules) in the *ovary*. The fertilising male cell is carried down by a tube which, sprouting from the pollen-grain, finds its way down the style and enters an ovule through a small hole called the *micropyle*. Fusion of the male cell from the pollen with the female cell formed in the ovule then takes place, and the growth of the new plant follows.

The *perianth segments* are six in number, and like the stamens are arranged in two ranks, or whorls, the three outer being the lower on the axis. The cumbrous term ' perianth segments ' has been used over a long period. Limbus, or limb, used by Linnæus and Herbert, is no better when one is obliged to speak of a section of the limb.

Perianth is a botanical term used for the sepals and petals of a flower taken together and regarded as surrounding the essential organs of reproduction, the stamens and pistil.

It is more especially used for those flowers in which the outer whorl of floral leaves, the sepals, closely resembles the inner world, the petals. The word tepal, an anagram of petal, has been used for both sepals and petals when they are much alike, as in Lilium, Colchicum, Crocus and other monocotyledonous flowers, but has never been in general use. In Narcissus the outer segments (the sepaline) are usually broader than the inner (petaline), and obviously must be a trifle longer so as to enclose them. All six are furnished at their tips with a small point, or mucro, which is a great asset from an artistic point of view to the outline of the flower.

It is designed, however, not only for ornament, but for a very real use to the opening flower. It may be noticed that the mucro of an outer segment is more conspicuous than that of an inner. This is due to a second small organ, a little white pad, or hook, which grows on its inner surface from the base of the mucro and points towards the centre of the flower. Before the flower opens the mucros of the inner segments are placed in the cavities formed by the pads of the outer segments. Each pad covers and holds in place one half of each of the mucros of the two inner segments next to it on either side, while the remaining half of each of these mucros is tucked away under the pad of the outer segment that is next beside it. Thus the three pads form a lock to hold the three inner mucros firmly in position, until the final lengthening of the outer segments lifts the pads apart, and all six segments are freed to fly open suddenly and to expose the floral organs, now ready to do their appointed work.

This fascinating and effective mechanism is found in many other Amaryllids and in Hemerocallis and other Liliaceous plants, but nowhere is it plainer to study, or more charming in its presence, than in the Daffodil.

The *corona* is the most distinctive character in the genus Narcissus. Its nature and origin have puzzled botanists, and many different opinions on both have been set forth.

The oldest writers, Clusius, Bauhin, Swertius and

others, used the terms tube and calyx for it. Linnæus
called it a nectary (nectarium), others a paracorolla,
and English writers have used crown, cup or trumpet,
according to its various shapes and lengths.

Dr. Masters wrote that he preferred the term
'corona' as comprehensive of all the varieties, and he
regarded it not as a distinct organ or set of organs, as
was at one time supposed, but as a mere secondary
outgrowth, of use probably in directing insects in
which way they should go.

This view is strengthened by the observed facts regarding the ontogeny of the Narcissus flower, that is,
the manner of development of its different parts at
various stages of growth. Dr. A. H. Church has
pointed out in his valuable book *Floral Mechanism*
that by July all the floral members are laid down, and
have assumed their definite occupations before any
trace of the corona appears. He continues: ' Sections
of buds taken in August show that this remarkable
structure (i.e. the corona) arises as an outgrowth of
the tissues between the bases of the perianth segments
and stamens, the first trace of it being noticed between
the insertions of the filaments; it then becomes continuous as a ring-growth all round the edge of the
receptacle-tube and presents the appearance of an
extension of the edge of the crater. There is no need,
however, to insist on its being a " receptacular " formation; it is distinctly a new and secondary feature of
great biological importance which has no relation to
the primary structure of the floral shoot, but is a part
of the secondary mechanism.'

The first appearance of the coronal growth between
the insertion of the filaments suggests an affinity with
the stipular adjuncts to filaments found in many
Liliaceous plants, such as Brodiæa, Allium and Tul-
baghia. This view was put forward by Pax (*Morpho-
logie*, p. 219), who gave a series of flowers showing

transitions from simple stipular outgrowths on each stamen to a full corona, as in Eucharis and Pancratium. Perhaps evidence for this might be found in the six-cleft corona of N. viridiflorus, in which the lobes occur alternately with the stamens so that the clefts appear opposite the centre of each perianth segment. Then the three-cleft corona of N. serotinus might be regarded as a step towards the six-lobed and entire coronas of less primitive forms.

Mr. W. C. Worsdell in *Principles of Plant-Teratology* follows Celakovsky's theory stated in his *Ueber die Bedeutung und den Ursprung der Paracorolle der Narcissen* (*Bull. internat. Acad. Sci. de Bohème*, 1898). Both based their views chiefly on abnormalities they observed in extremely erratic developments in double-flowered forms of N. Tazetta, and believed that the corona has been derived by petaloid transformation of the upturned basal lobes of the versatile anthers, and subsequent fusion thereof to form a continuous ring.

Double forms of N. Tazetta produce such a vast number of different kinds of malformation, that it seems to me rather unreasonable to deduce the natural evolution of an organ from certain obviously abnormal monstrosities. I have observed rudiments of filaments and anthers arising from various portions of similar ascidia and conglomerations of petaloid and coronal substance as those Celakovsky figures. Some of these suggested that the additional whorls were not derived from transformed stamens, but were proliferations of the perianth tube itself, bearing malformed portions of perianth segments, corona and one or more stamens.

In N. poeticus fl. pl. the central additional whorls are composed of white perianth segments bearing very small coronal lobes as outgrowths of the white portion, and below these there are long, stalk-like portions, of the substance and green coloration of the perianth tube, with a tendency to become tubular, looking like

3

successive repetitions of dialysed portions of an inner perianth tube produced by proliferation.

It is generally found that the single pistil of normal forms has been replaced in double flowers by three semicylindrical, petaloid bodies of various widths, for the most part white or greenish white.

Baillon (*Sur le development des fleurs à couronne : Adansonia* 1 [1860], p. 90) regarded the corona both in Pancratium and Narcissus as a late development of the floral axis at the base of the perianth, appearing after the stamens and carpels, which in Narcissus becomes a subsequent growth elevated on the corolla tube, while in Pancratium it rises to form a staminal cup with the bases of the filaments. He considered it a disc-like development of the floral axis, comparable with the honey-secreting disc frequent in flowers.

If the corona of Narcissus were formed from stipular bases of stamens fused as in Pancratium, Eucharis, etc., surely we might expect to find occasional reversions in which the stamens were carried up by filaments adnate to the corona, so that some portion of the filament stood free from the rim of the corona bearing an anther protruding beyond it. I have seen nothing like that.

Eichler (*Bluthendiagramme* 1, p. 157) and others prefer to consider it a component part of the corolla, that is to say, a ligular outgrowth comparable with those of Silene and other Caryophyllaceæ.

Dr. Church concludes thus: ' The corona as the most recent feature of the flower is relatively small in N. poeticus and N. Tazetta, and has not in those types attained such importance as to constitute a bell-type of flower; the most primitive case being found in N. Broussonetii . . . in which it only exists as a mere annular ridge at the end of the perianth tube.

' The corona thus appears to have arisen as a continuation of ridged outgrowths of the rim of the receptacle tube between the perianth and the andrœ-cium, which had the effect of forming a guard, and limiting the entrance to the floral tube, this being in fact a very general phenomenon in other types in which the floral mechanism involves a tube-principle (cf. Vinca, Myosotis, Agrostemma).'

He adds in a footnote: ' A closely comparable but wholly independent evolution in the American types Eucharis and Hymenocallis leads to the production of a zone of growth in the same region, which differs in that it elevates the filaments of the stamens on a similar cup.'

These, then, are some of the divergent views that have been expressed by those who have dealt with the morphology of the corona. It requires more study before a definite opinion can be pronounced. I may say, however, that if further work on the subject should lead to the view that ligular outgrowth from the perianth is a more correct conclusion than a fusion of the stipules of stamens, I should be ready to applaud that decision.

The outstanding argument against this that I feel requires explanation is founded on the six-cleft corona of N. viridiflorus, which closely resembles the still more rudimentary coronal lobes to be seen in Tapein-anthus humilis of Herbert (Carregnoa lutea of Boissier).

This minute plant with a very fugitive yellow flower occurs in Southern Spain and Morocco. It flowers in October, and its filiform leaves appear with, or soon after, the flowers. It is figured by Herbert on Pl. 22 of vol. 33 of the *Botanical Register* for 1847. It is very little known, being so small and doubtless difficult to cultivate in England.

The minute star-shaped flower has the shortest imaginable perianth tube, and generally only one is borne on the slender scape. Mr. Edwards kindly sent me flowering specimens from Gibraltar early in Novem-

ber, 1933, and I was able to observe the six minute
scales that appear in the throat of the flower, above the
stamens which are inserted in two ranks. The rudimentary corona varies in having the six scales sometimes entire, sometimes twice-cleft, and also occasionally almost too small to be observed.

Willkomm figures in his *Illustrationes*, t. lxxiv., A,
a very remarkable plant as Carregnoa dubia of Perez-
Lara. Two specimens were found near Jerez de la
Frontera on October 14th, 1875, by Mr. Perez-Lara,
one more in 1882, and apparently not again. It grew
among N. serotinus and Tapeinanthus humilis, and
may be a natural hybrid between them.

The jointed scape shown in the specimen from which
the illustration was drawn is probably the result of
uneven shrinkage in drying. Certain of its characters
are intermediate between the two genera, particularly
the longer perianth tube and the stamens projecting
less from the throat than in Tapeinanthus, also the
whiter flower and rather larger coronal scales.

This possible hybrid between Narcissus and Tapeinanthus is evidence pointing to some small North African
Amaryllid as a common ancestor of Narcissus and
perhaps a more primitive form of Leucoium than is
found in L. nicaeense, which is not greatly unlike
Tapeinanthus except in being more robustly formed
and having a pendent flower.

We ought, then, to regard N. serotinus, viridiflorus
and Broussonetii as primitive forms, and to find the
most highly specialised in those with bell-shaped
trumpets of the maximum length. In these the
corona has reached its highest development and func-
tions as a pollen protector in flowers adapted for pollination by the larger types of bees.

N. Bulbocodium has gone a step farther and has
developed a certain amount of zygomorphy, in a somewhat asymmetrical corona and curved stamens and

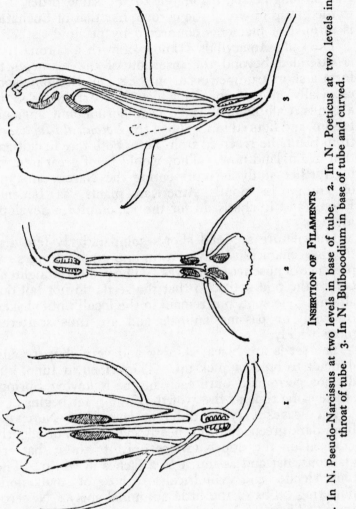

INSERTION OF FILAMENTS

1. In N. Pseudo-Narcissus at two levels in base of tube. 2. In N. Poeticus at two levels in
throat of tube. 3. In N. Bulbocodium in base of tube and curved.

pistil, somewhat on the lines of that curious plant
Elisena longipetala, belonging to the same order, but
to the group in which the corona, like that of Eucharis,
is formed of filaments connected by petaloid tissue.

The only Amaryllids I know of with a corona that
is extended beyond the insertion of the filaments to
form a short trumpet occur in the genus Stenomesson,
especially in two species which Herbert included in
a genus Callithamna as C. viridiflorum and angusti-
folium, and figured in t. 3866 of the *Botanical Magazine*,
from plants he received from Peru, both rare in cultivation in England now.   They would be of great interest
for further study as representing the Narcissean type
of corona in South American plants, as Ismene,
Elisena and Eucharis do for the Pancratiform development.

The mature seedpod shows comparatively few distinctive characters, save in unimportant degrees of
presence or absence of grooves.   The pedicel straightens
before the pod splits, so that the seeds do not fall out
all on to one spot, but remain in the loculi until shaken
by wind or passing animals and are thus scattered
more widely.

The seeds are black, shining and very slippery and
difficult to hold or pick up.   They ripen in June, but
do not germinate until early in the following Spring,
at the same time as the growth of the plant begins.

The leaves vary in different species of Narcissus
from dark green, filiform, nearly cylindrical, or slightly
grooved on the upper surface only, to those that are
glaucous, flat and as much as 2 inches in width.   The
most slender and cylindrical are those of small, non-
flowering bulbs of the little autumnal species N. serotinus.   Those of N. viridiflorus are stouter and sometimes slightly grooved on one side.   This is most
noticeable in the case of an offset bulb, bearing its
solitary leaf while still enclosed within the tunic of

the stronger bulb, which bears the flowering scape. The otherwise very slight groove is then accentuated by the pressure of the scape at an early stage of growth.

N. Jonquilla's shining, deep green leaves are so much like those of a rush as to have suggested its name, but even these have a flatter or grooved side, which is still more apparent in the laxer leaves of the tiny N. juncifolius.

Leaves channelled on the upper surface and semi-cylindrical beneath occur in varieties of N. Bulbocodium, very slender in the white monophyllus and tenuifolius, but sometimes $\frac{1}{4}$ inch wide in citrinus. A similar range is found in triandrus forms.

N. odorus, intermedius and gracilis, supposed hybrids of Jonquilla, have wider leaves with a concave, channelled upper surface, shining and deep green on both sides.

In the Tazetta group there is a range from the glaucous, narrow leaves of N. dubius to the wide, deep green leaves in papyraceus, italicus and many garden forms.

Ajax forms, and their hybrids with poeticus, generally have glaucous leaves, and in some of the seedlings from maximus they are nearly as blue as in that parent. Leaves of these cross-bred varieties are sometimes of a pale yellowish green and somewhat flimsy; they bend over when half grown and scorch and die off early in warm seasons. This is very noticeable in ' Sunrise '.

The most interesting structural points of Narcissus leaves are found at their opposite ends. The tips in flat forms are thickened and constricted to form a spoon-shaped hollow which with its thicker edges gives a strength that is of great use to the young leaves when thrusting their way through the soil. Except in the solitary-leaved autumnal species, the leaves of Narcissus are arranged face to face, and in their early

stages are bound together by two, three, or more
sheathing leaves, of which the innermost is longest and
reaches to the level of the soil.   Two to six leaves thus
bound together, with their concave tips fitting one within
the other, form a very powerful, rounded spearhead
which, urged upward by growth from below, forces a
way through the earth.   Once above the surface the
tallest sheathing leaf grows but little and the true
leaves push out into the air.

At its lower end in the heart of the bulb each leaf,
except the innermost of a flowering bulb, becomes
tubular, and this portion, as described on page 23,
thickens and stores up nourishment, ultimately forming
one of the fleshy scales of the new bulb.

The leaves, as well as the stems and bulb scales,
while in active growth are full of viscous sap which
contains a vast number of the sharply pointed crystals
called raphides, generally present in members of the
Amaryllis family, and so irritant to soft animal tissues
that they protect the plants from grazing animals.

M. Correvon pointed out to me the part that the
wild Narcissi of Alpine slopes play in the formation
of rich surface soil.   The bulbs are generally found at
a considerable depth, whence their roots descend
further still and absorb food from the mineral constit-
uents in solution in the soil.   These rise with the sap
and help to build up the leaves, and are added to the
surface soil when the leaves decay.

IV

CLASSIFICATION

A PERFECT classification of Narcissus does not exist, though many able botanists have attempted its provision. It should contain clear distinctions between species, provide tested pedigrees of intermediate forms suspected of hybrid origin, and be sufficiently simple to be used both in the garden and for shows.

The first requirement would entail many years of work in tracking down reputed wild species to their native stations and carefully observing their range of distribution and degree of variation.

Another life-time would be necessary to test their stability or variability when raised from seed, and whether certain intermediate forms could be reproduced by crossing distinct parents. Chromosome study might assist in this, but it appears that in Narcissus the chromosomes do not vary widely enough to afford much help.

Examination of the attempts made by botanists shows that doctors have differed so widely that it would be disastrous to swallow a prescription that was not founded on their common points of agreement. Differences of opinion have been so wide that the Index Kewensis includes no fewer than thirty-one other generic names that have been used for dividing what J. G. Baker regarded as one genus under its oldest name of Narcissus. He considered that it included only sixteen species, whereas well over four hundred specific names have been used.[1]

[1] It is interesting to compare this with the genus Senecio, which perhaps contains as widely divergent forms as any. Though these

In modern times the rapid increase in the numbers of garden-raised varieties of Narcissi, the results of crossing and intercrossing of what were formerly easily distinguished groups, has added to the difficulty of a botanical arrangement.

The Royal Horticultural Society appointed a Committee in 1908 to consider the subject, and it was decided that although a classification on natural and botanical lines would be both desirable and interesting, it could not be so useful for garden and show purposes as one mainly based on the comparative lengths of the perianth and the corona and their coloration.

The lists of names classified on these lines have been found very useful, and though the last one issued in 1933 contains over six thousand names, there are very few varieties that are so much on the borderline between two divisions as to lead to difficulties in judging.

This classification consists of eleven divisions, as follows:

DIVISION I—TRUMPET DAFFODILS

Distinguishing character—Trumpet or crown as long as or longer than the perianth segments.

(*a*) Varieties with yellow or lemon-coloured trumpets, and perianth of same shade or lighter (but not white).

(*b*) Varieties with white trumpet and perianth.

(*c*) Bicolor varieties, i.e. those having a white or whitish perianth and a trumpet coloured yellow, lemon or primrose, etc.

---

range from Groundsel and others with inconspicuous flowers to the gorgeous forms of S. Cineraria; from ivy-like climbing plants to succulents with fleshy stems as in the Kleinia group; or tall shrubs with large leaves as in S. Petasites; only sixty-four generic names have been proposed for this genus of over twelve hundred species, many of which seem to have taken to fancy dress.

DIVISION II—INCOMPARABILIS

Distinguishing character—Cup or crown not less than one-third, but less than equal to, the length of the perianth segments.

- (*a*) Yellow shades with or without red colouring on the cup.
- (*b*) Bicolor varieties with white or whitish perianth, and self-yellow, red-stained or red cup.

DIVISION III—BARRII (INCORPORATING BURBIDGEI)

Distinguishing character—Cup or crown less than one-third the length of the perianth segments.

- (*a*) Yellow shades, with or without red colouring on the cup.
- (*b*) Bicolor varieties, with white perianth and self-yellow, red-stained or red cup.

DIVISION IV—LEEDSII

Distinguishing character—Perianth white, and cup or crown white, cream or pale citron, sometimes tinged with pink or apricot.

- (*a*) Cup or crown not less than one-third, but less than equal to, the length of the perianth segments.
- (*b*) Cup or crown less than one-third the length of the perianth segments.

DIVISION V—TRIANDRUS HYBRIDS

All varieties obviously containing N. triandrus blood, such as Queen of Spain, Earl Grey, Eleanor Berkeley, Moonstone, Agnes Harvey, etc.

- (*a*) Cup or crown not less than one-third, but less than equal to, the length of the perianth segments.
- (*b*) Cup or crown less than one-third the length of the perianth segments.

DIVISION VI—CYCLAMINEUS HYBRIDS

DIVISION VII—JONQUILLA HYBRIDS

All varieties of N. Jonquilla parentage, such as Buttercup, odorus, etc.

DIVISION VIII—TAZETTA (GARDEN FORMS AND HYBRIDS)

To include N. Tridymus, poetaz varieties, the Dutch varieties of Polyanthus Narcissus, N. biflorus and N. Muzart.

DIVISION IX—POETICUS VARIETIES

DIVISION X—DOUBLE VARIETIES

DIVISION XI—VARIOUS

To include N. Bulbocodium, N. cyclamineus, N. triandrus, N. juncifolius, N. gracilis, N. Jonquilla, N. Tazetta (wild forms), N. viridiflorus, etc.

Some of these divisions may call for expansion in the future, such as making a separate subdivision for lemon-yellow, self-coloured Trumpets and for Leedsii varieties with pink cups.

It will be of interest to some readers to follow the growth of our knowledge of the kinds of Narcissi as shown in the writings of botanists from early times to the present day.

Theophrastus, the first of these, wrote his *Enquiry into Plants* about 300 B.C. He describes three plants used for garlands, which were called by some Narcissus, by others Leirion. One of these flowered in Autumn and is possibly a Sternbergia (but see under N. serotinus). In another passage he states that Narcissus and Leirion flower after Leucoion—in early Spring. One of these is almost certain to have been the universally grown N. Tazetta, the chief wild species in Greece.

Pliny compiled his great work *The History of the World* in the first century A.D. He repeats much from Theophrastus in even greater confusion, and describes three somewhat apocryphal kinds which are purple, grass green and white with a purple bell within, and all of them autumnal.

Dioscorides, contemporary with Pliny, was chiefly concerned with the medical properties of plants, and only describes Narcissus as white with a saffron or purple centre.

The *Herbal* of the Belgian Dodoens is most easily consulted in Lyte's English translation of 1578—he figures and describes five kinds: N. poeticus, two forms of Tazetta, Clusius's juncifolius and Pseudo-Narcissus, which he names Crowbels, and Bastarde Narcissus.

Lobel classified plants according to the peculiarities of their leaves, which gave him little choice for any original ideas for Narcissus. The greatest number of forms recognised by him are represented by the twenty-one wood-block illustrations in the album of figures without text published by Plantin in 1581 and again in 1591. The greater number of these blocks were used in other works published by Plantin, and especially in those of Clusius. Lobel divided the kinds into those with wide leaves, including poeticus, Tazetta, elegans (called serotinus) and Ajax; followed by those with narrow leaves, placing the double-flowered eystettensis after Bulbocodium and triandrus and before Jonquilla, juncifolius and the leafless serotinus.

Clusius in the *Hispanica* of 1576, and more fully in the *Historia* of 1601, provides the first really important critical review of the genus. In him we find a keen observer, who travelled to collect plants, and so had a first-hand knowledge of living specimens. His wide knowledge of Greek, Latin and contemporary languages and literature helped him to compare his ascertained facts with previously expressed opinions, and to make the *Historia* a rich treasury of sound knowledge that is always worth consulting. Later writers quote or incorporate much from Clusius, but it is safest to refer to the original.

His arrangement is as follows:

I. Single-flowered: (*a*) Wide-leaved, including four Tazetta forms, and, sad to relate, followed by N. indicus, which is Sprekelia. (*b*) Narrow-leaved—apparently odorus, Jonquilla and intermedius.

II. Double-flowered—three varieties of Tazetta, the mention only of a large yellow which failed to grow, and two forms of poeticus.

III. The leafless serotinus.

IV. Pseudo-Narcissus, containing eystettensis, two Spanish Ajax varieties; and Bulbocodium as Pseudo-N. juncifolius, including the yellow and white Hoop Petticoats.[1]

The first Appendix contains N. juncifolius, and Appendix II. contains incomparabilis, named oblongo-calice, and a double yellow form of Pseudo-Narcissus. Appendix III. contains triandrus and alpestris (moschatus Haw.).

These appendices are difficult to find, being generally bound in different books. The first follows the *Historia* at p. 253. The second is generally placed to follow the *Exoticorum*, Libri X. The third is called *Appendicis alterius Auctarium* and should follow the second.

In *Curae posteriores*, p. 11, Clusius further defines his

---

[1] Three Sternbergias are placed after serotinus and Pseudo-Narcissus.

classification according to wide or narrow leaves, single or double flowers, and after that as vernal or autumnal.

Tabernaemontanus, whose real name was Jacob Theodor, produced a herbal in 1588 as *Neuw Kreuterbuch*; the illustrations only as *Eicones Plantarum* in 1590; and subsequent editions of the whole work appeared in 1613 and 1664.

The figures are mostly reproduced from Bock, Fuchs, Dodoens and Clusius. There are nineteen of Narcissus and one each of a Pancratium and a Sternbergia. The Narcissi are arranged chiefly by being many-flowered or one only to a scape. Some of the figures are crude and absurd: one has a bulb like a fir-cone, another is the copy of Plantin's woodcut of N. serotinus, in which the wrinkles of the stem are so much exaggerated that they misled later writers as to their nature.

Gerard's *Herbal* was published in 1597 by John Norton, illustrated by the blocks used by Tabernaemontanus, which Norton had purchased. Gerard arranged them in a different order and provided them with English names and descriptions which give the impression that he had very slight personal knowledge of some of the plants. However, his description of the difficulty of cultivating N. Tazetta fl. pl. in England is evidently from first-hand experience. He used Plantin's figure for it, the only one that is not from the set used in Tabernaemontanus's *Herbal*.

The second edition, 'very much enlarged and amended by Thomas Johnson', published in 1633, and again without alteration in 1636, is better known and more frequently quoted than the first. Johnson had the advantage of making this enlargement after the publication of Clusius's works, and when the publishing firm of Adam Islip, Joice Norton and Richard Whitaker, who had replaced John Norton, could procure Plantin's blocks for the illustrations.

The first edition had fifteen figures of Narcissus, the second thirty, of which that used for the double-flowered N. Tazetta is the only one occurring in both. It should be noted by those who use the later edition that Johnson always marks his additions to the texts by a double dagger (‡) at their commencement and finish, and that a similar sign is placed before the numeral of the headings to illustrations of plants not included in the first edition.

Bauhin's *Pinax Theatri Botanici* of 1623 is the first methodical register of the plant names of previous writers. It was the work of Caspar, the younger of the two botanist brothers after whom Linnæus named the genus Bauhinia, because, as he explained, its leaves are two-lobed, as it were two springing from one base, like the two equally renowned brothers Jean and Caspar Bauhin.

He arranged the various names used by previous botanists as synonyms under the name he selected for each plant, thus converting chaos into an order that was recognised as authoritative up to the time of Linnæus, who quoted from it throughout the *Species Plantarum*. This makes it an indispensable link between the old and the new nomenclatures.

The *Pinax* divides Narcissus into ten groups, of which the second, N. exoticus, is composed of Brunsvigia and Sprekelia, and the tenth of Pancratium. The others, Narcissi as we now understand them, are chiefly divided by width of leaves, and again by form of corona (calyx), narrow, oblong or short; and those with double flowers are placed in group nine.

Tournefort in *Institutiones rei herbariae* (1700-1719) repeats Bauhin's names and some of the synonyms in the same order as in the *Pinax*.

Parkinson's *Paradisus* of 1629 contains a host of names and figures of Narcissi. His main idea is to divide true Narcissi from Pseudo-Narcissi according to the ' middle cup or chalice ', which in the latter is as long, or a little longer, than the ' outer leaves that doe encompasse it, so that it seemeth rather like a trunke or long nose than a cup or chalice, such as almost all the Narcissi or true Daffodils have '.   These he subdivides by the form of leaves, number of flowers, double flowers and season, following previous authors.

His diligence in collecting what had been already written and the charm of the quaint English in which he recounts it all, together with the numerous illustrations, have led to his work being somewhat overvalued as a sound authoritative account.   Most of the figures are crude copies, engraved in England by Switzer, of Plantin's blocks and the beautiful copper plates of Crispin de Pas and the *Theatrum Florae*.   Fig. 3 on p. 89 is an example of what can be done in exaggeration if compared with Clusius's block of N. serotinus; and Fig. 3 on p. 75, ' the early purple ringed Daffodil ', shows what Switzer has done to de Pas' beautiful Fig. 19.

Rudbeck's *Campi Elysii*, published in 1701 at Upsala, contains a great number of figures of Narcissi, but almost all of his figures can be recognised as copies from those in other works.   They are exaggerated and badly drawn and very unreliable, so much so that Dean Herbert refers to them as ' garbled '.

The publication of Linnæus's *Species Plantarum* in 1753 is the starting-point of all recent classifications. His treatment of Narcissus contrasts sharply with previous ideas, and the hundred or so forms named by Bauhin and Tournefort are reduced to six species which, in the Second Edition of 1762, though enumerated as thirteen, are but eleven, as his calathinus and trilobus are found to be varieties of his odorus.   His species are differentiated first by the number of flowers to a spathe, whether many or one, and then by a flat or campanulate corona and wide or subulate leaves.

4

Linnæus had no opportunity of observing the distribution of the genus in Southern and Western Europe, and the limited number of forms in his herbarium suggests that he encountered very few in the living state in his later years. He regarded as garden varieties those he observed in Holland while he was in charge of Clifford's garden near Haarlem, explaining in the *Hortus Cliffortianus* (p. 134) that though Boerhavius regards the species of Narcissus as forty-seven, Ray fifty, Tournefort about a hundred and the Haarlem gardeners, who produce new species every year by art, as still more, he intends to examine only those created by the Almighty—' ego solum creata omnipotentis rimare studio '.

Robert Anthony Salisbury, the secretary of the Horticultural Society of London, 1805-1816, and author of the *Paradisus Londinensis*, described some Narcissi in *Prodromus stirpium in horto ad Chapel Allerton vigentium*, published in 1796.

His chief work upon the genus was included in his papers ' On the Cultivation of Rare Plants ', read before the Horticultural Society in 1812 and published in vol. i. of the *Transactions* in that same year. It is important because he published therein six of the genera into which he subdivided Narcissus, but, as Herbert has pointed out in his *Amaryllidaceae*, ' without any explanation of his views '. These are Ajax, Corbularia, Ganymedes, Hermione, Philogyne and Queltia, all of which were adopted by Haworth, and excepting Philogyne by Herbert.

Salisbury afterwards added nine other genera, which fortunately, finding no supporters, need not claim our attention. In the account in the *Transactions* he has attempted to identify the names of previous authors for the forms he regarded as species, and quotes figures from Clusius, Pas, Trew, Redouté, the *Botanical Magazine*, and other sources; refers to the Linnean

Herbarium and gives so many personal experiences and recollections of the histories of Narcissi that the paper is well worth studying, though so few of the names are in present use.

Adrian Hardy Haworth published his *Narcissorum Revisio* in 1819 as an adjunct to his *Supplementum Plantarum Succulentarum*, which is now a scarce book. In the preface he refers to three previous papers on Narcissi of his writing, one published by the Linnean Society in 1800, the second in the *Miscellanea Naturalia* in 1803, and the other in 1812 in the Appendix to his *Synopsis Plantarum Succulentarum*. The *Revisio* was written to amend the earlier descriptions, to include a further number of supposed species, and to divide them into distinct genera. He followed the lead of Salisbury, but provided definitions of the characters on which the genera were founded, none of which had been given by Salisbury. Here, then, we find the first definitions of numerous genera.

Haworth's most important work is the Monograph on the Subordo V. of Amaryllideae containing the Narcissineae, first published in the first volume of the Second Series of Sweet's *British Flower Garden* in 1831, and followed in November of the same year by a second, amended edition. In these the generic definitions remodelled from those of the *Revisio* are still so unsatisfactory that, as Dean Herbert pointed out in his *Amaryllidaceae*, ' it is utterly impossible that the scientific public should ever adopt his generic characters, because they are founded on trivial features, in some cases unfit even to support a specific distinction '.

Haworth had a keen eye for minute differences and an uncontrollable desire to make the most of them to enable him to create a genus, species or variety to which he could attach a name. Even a crude figure in an old book was sufficient evidence for the addition of another species with Latin and English names, though he had never seen such a plant. Besides numerous species he added nine new genera to the seven he adopted from Salisbury. The result is:

Genus.	Number of Species.	Type.
1. Corbularia	10	Hoop Petticoat
2. Ajax	24	Trumpet
*3. Oileus	5	abscissus
*4. Assaracus	2	calathinus
*5. Illus	2	triandrus
6. Ganymedes	5	pulchellus
*7. Diomedes	3	Macleayi
*8. Tros	2	poculiformis
9. Queltia	7	incomparabilis
*10. Schizanthes	1	Schizanthes
11. Philogyne	9	odorus
*12. Jonquilla	4	Jonquil
*13. Chloraster	2	viridiflorus
14. Hermione	54	Tazetta
*15. Helena	6	gracilis
16. Narcissus	12	poeticus

148

* Added by Haworth.

Haworth's work has the same kind of interest for the student as Salisbury's. His citations and identifications of figures, being brought up to a later date, are more valuable, but as an index rather than as authoritative botanical recognitions. Some of the English names describe minor characters aptly—as in ' the green-leaved cream-coloured ' and ' the glaucescent-leaved ' for two Tazetta forms closely allied. However, such as ' the slender straw-coloured ' for N. tenuior, and ' the short-tubed spread crown ' for obvallaris, and ' the great gash-crowned ' are perhaps better forgotten.

Herbert's *Amaryllidaceae*, published in 1837, remained the leading authority on that order until the appearance of J. G. Baker's *Handbook of Amaryllideae* in 1888. Dean Herbert reduced Haworth's sixteen genera to six by including Oileus under Ajax; Assaracus and Illus under Ganymedes; Diomedes, Tros, Schizanthes, Philogyne and Jonquilla under Queltia; Chloraster under Hermione; and Helena under Narcissus with poeticus.

He rejected as species those known from figures only, but described forty-five species and about a hundred and thirty varieties. Many of these he figured, though the greater proportion are represented by dissections only.

The work was issued in two states, with coloured or with plain plates; but the coloration where it occurs is only a slight wash, and in many instances dull or brown to represent that of dried specimens; therefore it adds more to the market value of the book than to its usefulness.

Continental authors have followed closely the lead of the British monographers Herbert and Baker.

Spach in his *Histoire naturelle des végétaux Phanerogames*, vol. xii., 1846, did little more than translate Haworth's work into French, but uses his generic names for sections of the one genus Narcissus. Roemer and Schultes also followed Haworth, but Kunth's *Enumeratio* of 1840 is modelled on Herbert's lines.

Parlatore dealt solely with Italian forms in his *Flora italica* of 1858; therefore he could omit Herbert's Corbularia and Ganymedes, which are all of Western origin, and by including Hermione in Narcissus he retained but three genera, the others being Ajax, and Queltia containing only incomparabilis and odorus.

The French Botanist Gay in 1859 reckoned the genera as seven, adding Aurelia (to cover N. Broussonetii) and Carregnoa (now Tapeinanthus); and retaining Corbularia, Ajax, Queltia, Ganymedes and Narcissus.

It is a relief to turn from these complicated views

to that of Baker, who associates all these genera, except Tapeinanthus, under Narcissus. In 1875 he contributed a *Review of the genus Narcissus* to Burbidge's *History*, stating therein that the extremes in structure shown by Narcissi were connected by sufficiently gradual and intermediate links as to be included in a single genus as planned by Linnæus. Baker then considered that not more than twenty should be regarded as species, the tests for which should include their being definitely known to occur in a wild state, and possessing sufficiently distinctive characters by which they can be separated.

The best strictly botanical classification extant is that on p. 2 of Baker's *Handbook of Amaryllideae*, 1888. It is based on the proportions of the corona and divided into three sections:

> *Magnicoronati*—Corona funnel-shaped or cylindrical, as long as the perianth segments, with Corbularia and Ajax as subsections, each containing but one species.

> *Mediocoronati*—Corona cup-shaped, about half as long as the perianth segments. Subsections, Ganymedes and Queltia.

> *Parvicoronati*—Corona small, obconic or saucer-shaped. Subsections, Hermione, corona uniform in texture; Eunarcissus, corona scariose at the edge; Aurelia, corona nearly obsolete.

Under these only sixteen species are grouped. Another eleven forms of hybrid origin bring the number up to twenty-seven, while twenty-six subspecies and thirteen varieties with Latin names are described.

Burbidge's *History*, referred to above, is *The Narcissus : its History and Culture*, by F. W. Burbidge, published in 1875. It contains forty-eight hand-coloured plates drawn by the author. They are rather stiff as to drawing and gay in colouring, but very useful for botanical reference. Mr. Burbidge was the Curator of the fine old garden of Trinity College, Dublin; a man of singular kindliness and personal charm, with a wide first-hand knowledge of plants, and a frequent contributor to the gardening journals of his day.

More recent books of note are the following:

The Book of the Daffodil, by the Rev. S. Eugene Bourne, vol. xvi. of the *Handbooks of Practical Gardening* published by John Lane. Mr. Bourne was Vicar of Dunstan, near Lincoln, where he cultivated Daffodils; he was also one of the best judges of a good flower. This book is the best concise and complete account of Narcissi up to the date of its publication early in the present century, dealing with them chiefly from the gardener's view, but including much botanical information.

The Rev. Joseph Jacob, Rector of Whitewell, contributed the volume on Daffodils to the *Present Day Gardening Series* published by Messrs. Jack. It contains eight plates coloured by a photographic process, and is full of practical information presented in the charming, simple style of that deservedly popular writer.

Daffodil Growing for Pleasure and Profit is the title of a wonderfully comprehensive work written by Mr. Albert F. Calvert in collaboration with the best authorities on the subject. It was published in 1929, and contains 412 pages of text and a series of 230 photographic illustrations of Narcissi of note. These pictures are outstanding in their excellence as portraits of the varieties as well as for the perfection of their reproduction.

The *Daffodil Year Book*, published by the Royal Horticultural Society, was started in 1913 and discontinued after its third year owing to the difficulties entailed by the Great War. Those three volumes have

by now become very scarce and difficult to procure. It
was revived in 1933, however, and it is hoped that its
yearly appearance may be long continued. Besides
the accounts of shows and the awards made by the
Royal Horticultural and other Societies during the
previous season, a number of important articles from
authoritative writers, portraits of celebrated raisers
and illustrations of plants that have received awards or
are of special interest, fill the 136 pages of the volume
for 1933. The 1934 volume contains 25 plates, a
frontispiece and 103 pages of text. Besides other
important articles, Mr. de Mot's on ' The Origin of
Double Daffodils ', and Mr. Gibson's on ' The Scillonian
Flower Industry ', are of special interest.

Mr. W. H. Pugsley has lately added two very important revisions of two Divisions of the genus.

The first, *N. poeticus and its allies*, was published
in 1915 as a *Supplement to the Journal of Botany*. It
is a most careful and critical work containing wonderfully complete references to herbarium specimens,
figures and earlier descriptions. Therein N. poeticus
is divided into two Series, I. Poetici with five species,
II. Radiiflori with four species. The nine species are
more generally considered as varieties or at the most
subspecies.

The second, *Monograph of Narcissus, subgenus Ajax*,
was published in the Royal Horticultural Society's
Journal, vol. lviii., part i., 1933. It is a larger and even
more important work, the result of much labour and
critical judgment. It is well illustrated, and questions
of nomenclature are cleared up effectively. The
author's bias is towards regarding more forms as of
specific standing than anyone has since Haworth and
Jordan.

V

Yellow Trumpet Daffodils

DIVISION I.*a*, varieties with yellow or lemon-coloured trumpets and perianth of same shade or lighter (but not white), is the R.H.S. definition for self-yellow trumpets.

It should be remembered that this is intended chiefly for garden and show purposes. Examples of yellow trumpets among wild, or reputedly wild, forms are N. obvallaris and the N. hispanicus group, including maximus. ' King Alfred ', ' Dawson City ', ' Sulphur ' and ' Magnificence ' are good examples of garden-raised varieties.

N. pallidus praecox (pallidiflorus Pugsley) is the only wild representative of the lemon-coloured trumpets. By natural affinity it belongs to the bicolors, as shall be explained later. Garden varieties include ' Seraphine ' (raised by van Tubergen), ' Brimstone ' (Engleheart), ' Disraeli ' (G. L. Wilson) and the small ' W. P. Milner ', though it has been classed as white and 1*b*.

Mr. Pugsley has arranged the more or less wild concolorous yellow forms as his series Lutei. Those in cultivation can be arranged under two group names, (1) N. hispanicus (Gouan) and (2) N. obvallaris (Salisbury).

N. hispanicus. The form known as N. maximus well deserves that name, but has no botanical right to it. The authority quoted for it is D. Don in connection with t. 286 of Sweet's *British Flower Garden*, Second Series, vol. iii. The figure and description, however, belong to a plant with wide, flat perianth segments, which is

Haworth's maximus, called by him ' the intermediate large yellow of Dutch gardens ', and is recognised by Pugsley as the well-known garden plant ' Henry Irving '. Curtis's figure, t. 51 in the *Botanical Magazine*, 1793, represents the true maximus with its dark yellow flowers, long, twisted perianth segments, a widely expanded, deeply gashed corona, and glaucous, spirally twisted leaves. Curtis and Haworth called this N. major, so it is best to follow Pugsley in using Gouan's prior name hispanicus, published in 1773 as a specific name to include as varieties large forms with self-yellow flowers of supposedly Spanish origin. This largest form then should become N. hispanicus var. maximus.

Wherever it has been especially well grown it has acquired further honorary titles such as ' Trinity College Variety ' in Dublin, ' Hale's Vase of Beaten Gold ' in Hartland's *Original Little Book of Daffodils*, 1887, and nowadays ' variety superbus ' of some.

The woodcut used by Lobel in the Latin and Flemish Editions of his *Stirpium Historia* and on p. 117 of his *Icones* represents the long trumpet with wide frilled edge very clearly. He called it ' N. totus luteus montanus Theoph. Hispanicus '.

Clusius used the same block for his Ps.-N. major Hispanicus, but in the text describes the flower as smaller than the English one. These blocks were used somewhat indiscriminately to illustrate different books, and this one was certainly drawn from the larger plant. The figure in Parkinson's *Paradisus* is poor, but his description is good. He calls it ' Pseudonarcissus aureus Hispanicus maximus ', and writes that ' it desires to be deep in the ground and therefore will run down, the one faire great yellow flower standing forth right, and not pendulous, consisting of six short and somewhat broad leaves, with a very great, large, and long trunk, of an equal largeness but open at the mouth and turning up the brimmes a little which are somewhat crumpled '.

There is no exact record of the locality from which this best form was introduced, and no specimen from a wild source exists in herbaria. Willkomm's localities for major are intended to include Clusius's small-flowered form and various others.

So for the present we should accept Nyman's view that it is rare in Spain, but frequently cultivated and sometimes subspontaneous in the south. Recent research shows that the chromosome number of maximus is twenty-one, lesser forms of the group having fourteen.

It is likely that our garden plant represents a large mutant which either appeared spontaneously in some rich meadow soil or under cultivation, and as long ago as the sixteenth century.

Maximus is one of the finest garden plants wherever it can be induced to settle down. Deep planting, in well-drained but rich soil, seems to suit its desires best, and so long as it flowers well it should not be disturbed, unless it is desired to encourage more rapid increase. Close to the seashore in Western England it flowers so early that in some seasons it is ready to cut for market by the end of January. The same stocks of bulbs taken further inland lose their early-flowering habit gradually year by year until they flower in early March in average seasons.

The great size of its rich yellow blooms, on stalks that can reach a height of 30 inches or more, will always attract attention even when grown alongside newer and larger varieties. The tube is dark green at its base and bright green up to the base of the perianth segments. A green streak runs up the middle of each, and is more conspicuous on the three outer, on which it reaches to the tip. They are twisted spirally so that the underside, especially in the inner ones, is brought into view for about $\frac{1}{2}$ inch.

N. major B., the upper flower in t. 1301 of the *Botanical Magazine*, stands a grade lower in colour and size. Salisbury renamed it A. propinquus in his *Prodromus*, but afterwards in *Transactions* of the Horticultural Society made it A. lacinularis. He states that it was cultivated at North Bierly in 1712, and was often sent accidentally among Dutch bulbs. Haworth chose Salisbury's earlier name and cites the *Bot. Mag.* major B. for propinquus; Herbert does the same in the *Amaryllidaceae*. The chief characters shown in this figure are the distinctly six-lobed trumpet and wide, only slightly twisted segments of a paler yellow than in maximus.

In his recent *Monograph of Ajax*, Mr. Pugsley writes: ' Propinquus has been almost lost to horticulture, and is perhaps most nearly represented by the popular garden plant known as " Golden Spur ", which is somewhat intermediate between the varieties propinquus and spurius, but larger than either.'

' Golden Spur ', as compared with Curtis's plate of propinquus, has a more reflexed mouth to the corona, with its six lobes more boldly toothed, and a less hooded perianth. It seems to have been newly introduced some time before 1886, as Hartland's *Original Little Book of Daffodils* for 1887 contains an illustration of it and states that it was named at the Conference held in 1886. It has been largely grown for market in England and Holland, being one of the best early yellow trumpets. To say that any new seedling is ' as good and earlier than Golden Spur ' would be high praise indeed.

Haworth invented the name *spurius* for the plant figured in Rudbeck's *Campi Elysii* in 1701 as ' Narcissus major luteus calice praelongo alter '. It is anyway an improvement on that pre-Linnean string of adjectives, but as in the second edition of his *Monograph* Haworth placed an asterisk against this ' species ', signifying

that it was ' unknown to author ', and seeing that
Rudbeck's figure shows a flower with seven segments,
it appears to be little more than guesswork to connect
them with the plant now grown as spurius. This is
rather more dwarf than the foregoing, and was listed
by Hartland of Cork in 1887 as ' spurius major, the
best Dutch form '.

None of these four varieties, or forms, thus grouped
under N. hispanicus is sufficiently represented in
herbaria from wild specimens to be regarded as more
than a mutant or seedling from some common parent.
It may be that the N. concolor Pl. 355 of Jordan's
Icones from Le Luc (Var) in the South of France
represents such a plant. It is very much like one
found by Colonel Enever Todd at about 5,000 feet in
the Sierra de la Nieva in South Spain. N. major of
gardens and of Dutch catalogues is the most similar
cultivated variety.

These all have a curious dark brown projection at the
apex of each of their anthers. It is most noticeable
in young flowers before the anthers have dehisced, but
unless covered over by loose pollen is visible until the
anthers wither and shrink. It is very distinct in
maximus, ' King Alfred ', ' Henry Irving ', obvallaris,
' Sulphur ', ' Goldbeater ', ' Orange Glory ' (a cyclamineus hybrid), and in some deep yellow incomparabilis seedlings, particularly in ' Havelock ', ' Arundel '
and ' St. Ives '.

Varieties in which these brown tips are present,
but smaller and less distinct, are ' Hamlet ', ' Golden
Spur ' and the white ' Beersheba ' among trumpets;
' Bodilly ' and ' Helios ' in incomparabilis; and ' White
Nile ' in Leedsii. They are absent in the Lent Lily
and all the bicoloured trumpets that I have examined.
They may be indications of the occurrence of some
form of the hispanicus group in a pedigree.

N. obvallaris, the Tenby Daffodil, has suffered sorely

in the hands of botanists. Many and various are the
names that have been applied to it.

It is a very distinct, dwarf and early, deep yellow
form, recognisable from a distance by its expanded,
six-lobed trumpet and the wide and flat perianth
segments, springing away almost at a right angle from
the wide upper portion of the tube. Thus it seems
to be a smaller, more chubby flower than it really is
by measure. Its brilliant yellow is almost the same as
the colouring of 'King Alfred', its texture is smooth
and the arrangement of the six segments so perfectly
symmetrical that few other trumpet Daffodils show
so perfectly the design of the two triangles formed by
the outlines of the inner and outer segments. Except
for somewhat dingy colouring (due to the difficulties
inherent with yellow pigments) the lower flower in
t. 1301 of the *Botanical Magazine* is a good portrait.

There it is called N. major var. γ. Salisbury named
it obvallaris, and Haworth continued using this name
in connection with the *Bot. Mag.* figure, but invented
the name A. lobularis for what he calls the ' Tenby
6-lobed Daffodil ' and even provided it with some
varieties. His hair-splitting eye and untiring diligence
seem solely responsible for these, and his rugilobus
(which is not the garden plant so named) and also
cambricus, of which he confesses he saw only one
withered specimen, should be regarded as synonyms
of obvallaris.

In Boswell Syme's Edition of *English Botany* (better
known as Sowerby's, from the illustrator of the first
edition, in the same way that we speak of Redouté's
Lilies and *Roses*) there is mention of a variety Brom-
fieldii. This is stated to grow at Tenby and in the
Isle of Wight, and to be Ajax lobularis of Haworth.

I regard N. obvallaris as the most perfect in proportion and texture of any deep yellow trumpet, and for
' close-up ' observation unlikely to be improved upon

unless it may be in constitution, for unhappily this little gem is not easily cultivated in the majority of gardens.

Bourne wrote that it was especially good in a cold frame. As a pot plant for very gentle forcing it will flower in February. In some Sussex gardens and where there is deep loamy soil it does well in grass.

' Santa Maria ' resembles a small and dwarf maximus and is particularly charming and distinct in outline. It has grown well for many years in the short turf at Wisley, seeding itself freely and for the most part retaining its individuality, though some of the seedlings show less of the external green markings than is desirable.

There is a good photographic portrait of it in the *Daffodil Year Book* for 1915, Fig. 6 showing the narrow twisted segments, but not the characteristic long, funnel-shaped tube of the perianth. This is over an inch in length and brilliantly green, but yellow in the six deep furrows corresponding with the divisions between the segments, the backs of which are marked with green lines down the centre.

The outline of the flower makes one wonder whether it can have arisen as a natural hybrid between one of the hispanicus group and N. Bulbocodium.

Mr. Pugsley proposes the name N. pallidiflorus to replace N. pallidus praecox, the unorthodox form that has been used in gardens ever since Peter Barr, senior, reintroduced the Bayonne form in 1882, and recognised it as Parkinson's Early Strawe-coloured Bastard Daffodil, Pseudonarcissus pallidus praecox of p. 99 of the *Paradisus*.

Parkinson described another plant on p. 73 as the Early Strawe-coloured Daffodil with a long cup, N. pallidus oblongo calice flavo praecox. This seems to belong to the group of Pyrenean hybrids with straight edges to the corona, of which Johnstonii,

Bernardii and montanus are examples. Burbidge thought Parkinson's long-cupped plant matched Barr's, and so treated it in *The Garden*, vol. xxv., p. 185, in 1884, though his illustration shows a form with a very much expanded and reflexed brim to the corona.

The Strawe-coloured Bastard Daffodil is clearly the one Parkinson intended for the Bayonne plant. He describes its 'trunke' as 'large with the brimmes turned up a little, the wings standing straight out and not flagging down like unto the Mountain kinds'. He says 'all the whole flower is of one even colour like that of lemon peel, but whiter, which usually we call a strawe colour'. This aptly describes the form most generally grown and plants that I collected in 1894 in a wood at Cambo near Bayonne, where it grew mixed with the bicoloured Pseudo-Narcissus of that neighbourhood. The pale form was scattered sparsely among the more numerous bicoloured type, of which I believe it to be a pale variant, and I have found that many of the self-sown seedlings from the pale forms I brought home are bicoloured. They inherit the praecox character and flower early, but too seldom the pallidus.

Some collected for me in Spain are taller, with much green in the tube, variable as to the brim of the corona from straight and crenate to six-lobed and coarsely dentate. The flowers are more erect than in the Bayonne plants, and the corona in some is deeper in colour than the perianth; they have brown tips to the anthers, a character associated with the deep yellow Spanish plants.

These may belong to Pugsley's form asturicus, and the semi-erect port, the green of the tube, the more glaucous leaves and brown-tipped anthers suggest that they are pallid derivatives from some hispanicus variety instead of Pseudo-Narcissus.

A bulb collected in a copse near Mont Louis in the

Eastern Pyrenees has a shorter scape, larger flower, more expanded brim to the corona, which is darker than the long, hooded perianth segments.

The form found near Ax-les-Thermes grows in pure colonies and is very vigorous, increasing readily under cultivation.

It is often stated that pallidiflorus seldom increases vegetatively. I am thankful to be able to state that I have many large clumps which have grown from single bulbs.

A large colony exists in a spinney in Cornwall which has spread widely from a few planted bulbs. They vary considerably in form and colour, but it can be plainly seen that individual seedlings have increased to form clumps. Those nearest to the original planting are truer to type than those on the outskirts of the colony; many of the latter show traces of crossing with other races, some being bicoloured, others nearly self-yellow.

These facts imply that pallid forms of at least three races of trumpet Daffodils have been introduced to gardens under the name pallidus praecox:

1. The Bayonne form derived from N. Pseudo-Narcissus.

2. The Spanish form asturicus of Pugsley from N. hispanicus.

3. The form Pugsley calls N. macrolobus β pallescens from the variable bicoloured race of the Central Pyrenees, of which my plant from Mont Louis is a specimen.

5

VI

WHITE TRUMPET DAFFODILS

THIS IS Division I.*b* of the R.H.S. Classification.

Until further evidence is available it is best to believe that there is no more than one pure white species of Ajax or Trumpet Daffodils, which is truly wild. This is the plant generally known in gardens as N. moschatus of Haworth. It was figured and described by Clusius in the *Auctarium* to the *Second Appendix* to his *Historia* as Pseudonarcissus albo flore. The woodcut clearly shows the drooping flower and narrow leaves characteristic of the plant. It was sent to Clusius by Venerius from the Pyrenees in 1604.

Parkinson's Ps.-N. hispanicus minor albus (Fig. 4 on p. 101) looks as though it had been copied, and not too well, from Clusius's block. Johnson adds Clusius's block and a short paraphrase of his description in the enlarged edition of Gerard, but it is quite likely that neither he nor Parkinson knew the plant otherwise than through the account given by Clusius.

So attractive and remarkable a plant surely would have been figured in an early number of the *Botanical Magazine* had it been in cultivation at the close of the eighteenth century. Haworth's quick eye for minute differences must have noticed that the *Bot. Mag.* t. 1300 cited by him for moschatus (misprinted as 1800 in his *Monograph*) was not the same as Parkinson's (Fig. 4, p. 101), if he had ever seen a living flower of Clusius's plant.

As Pugsley points out, Haworth has cited Parkinson's Ps.-N. hispanicus flore albo minor for his moschatus and also under cernuus. It is possible that in the

66

latter case the word minor is a misprint for major.[1]
If we correct minor to major under Haworth's cernuus,
and add t. 101, Fig. 3, the reference will agree with
Parkinson. Haworth mentions the albiflorae he had
seen, viz. albicans and cernuus, and omits doing so
for his tortuosus and moschatus.

Salisbury seems to have been misled by Johnson's
and Parkinson's habits of including in their works
descriptions lifted from Clusius when he stated that
moschatus was as common in Parkinson's days as it
was scarce in his.

Mr. Edward Buxton in 1884 and Mr. George Maw
in 1885 rediscovered it in the Spanish Pyrenees, and
Mr. Colgan in 1890 collected some bulbs on the limestone plateau of the Gaulis in upper Aragon. They
throve in his garden in Ireland, and there is a good illustration of a clump of them in *The Garden*, September
26th, 1896.

F. W. Burbidge in the accompanying text wrote: ' It
is curious to note that although this plant was known
in Continental gardens in the late sixteenth and early
seventeenth century days, when it was accurately
represented by Dutch and Belgian painters, yet it was
apparently quite lost sight of until rediscovered by
Mr. Buxton in the Val d'Arrases in the early Summer
of 1884.'

He continues that he considers the specimen named
moschatus in the Linnean herbarium is probably
N. cernuus of our present-day gardens, and the larger
plant of Dutch gardens is N. albicans, which Haworth
called ' the greatest Spanish white ', but which ' has
never been found wild in Spain or elsewhere. . . . The
only really wild white Daffodil known is the true

---

[1] Several misprints occur on this page of Haworth's *Monograph*.
He cites a figure of hispanicus maximus albidus as Fig. 1 on
Parkinson's p. 101, but Parkinson has no figure of his maximus
albidus.

N. moschatus now alluded to, and from which it seems . . . all other white variations now known in gardens have descended from seed '.

This view of the identity of Linnæus's specimen is upheld by Pugsley, and the name N. moschatus L. should be used for the plant hitherto known as N. cernuus. Linnæus's specimen was grown in the Upsala Garden and resembles Sydenham Edwards's figure, t. 1300 of the *Botanical Magazine*, and not the little Pyrenean plant.

Therefore a new name became necessary for the wild Pyrenean plant, and it now appears in Pugsley's *Monograph* as *N. alpestris* Pugsley.

As moschatus it is well shown in Moon's plate of white Daffodils in *The Garden*, July 26th, 1890, and again in a photograph taken in the Wargrave Plant Farm. Tortuosus minor on the end sheet of Hartland's list, 1887, is another portrait of it, and also No. 1 on p. 9.

Whatever name we may use it will always be one of the most beautiful plants for a cool corner, preferably among small rocks where moss and slender ferns like Oakfern will grow. Seedlings appear spontaneously in such a position and vary as to size, but have never to my knowledge departed from their snowy whiteness. The nodding flowers look all the whiter in contrast with the deep green of their perianth tubes.

Hartland listed ' recently collected plants from the Pyrenees ' in 1887 as ' all snow white, and most varied in outline, for Gents' coats beautiful '.

Burbidge's Pl. 8, named cernuus, represents the moschatus of Haworth, now N. alpestris of Pugsley.

The differences in form between albicans, tortuosus and cernuus are well shown in an outline illustration in *The Garden*, June 2nd, 1883, p. 498.

N. albescens Pugsley. As N. albicans is a name used for a Corbularia by Sprengel in 1825, and is therefore invalid for an Ajax, Mr. Pugsley proposes N. albescens in its place.

It is finely figured in Sweet's *British Flower Garden*, Second Series, vol. ii., t. 145, and in Jordan's *Icones*, ccclvi. It is a tall plant with twisted glaucous leaves, but has almost disappeared from gardens to make way for more recent and finer white seedlings. A touch of sulphur in its colouring suggests its being a white seedling from a yellow species, perhaps the old major of gardens, crossed with the tiny N. alpestris.

N. moschatus L. The N. cernuus of gardens thus becomes N. moschatus of Linnæus. It is t. 1300 of the *Botanical Magazine*; also, perhaps the single, but certainly the double, flower figured in Sweet's *British Flower Garden*, Second Series, vol. ii., t. 101. Burbidge figured three forms of the double flower on Pl. 12 varying after the same manner found in the ' Van Sion ' double Daffodil. His Plate 7 represents the single-flowered N. cernuus of gardens. There is a good woodcut by him in Barr's *Ye Narcissus* on p. 36. The figure 2439 in Bailey's *Cyclopedia* is worth looking up as representing the ' cernuus of the trade.'

Ajax tortuosus, the great tortuose white, is the title Haworth conferred on the *Botanical Magazine* t. 924, Gawler's moschatus α and Salisbury's Ajax longiflorus. Having such a long, narrow trumpet and twisted perianth, it is a flower possessed of little merit, unless we take into account Salisbury's discovery that it smells of ginger. It has not been found in a wild state, and looks like the ill-proportioned flowers that are certain to occur in a large batch of seedlings, many of which were named and treasured for their whiteness in earlier times.

It is interesting to look at the lists of the eighties and to notice how many white Daffodils then listed have disappeared: such as 'William Goldring', described as snow white and dog eared, 1s. 6d. each; ' Colleen

Bawn ', twisted, propeller-like perianth segments and long, cylinder-like trumpet, 2s. 6d.; ' Leda ', perfumed like old oak timber; ' Gladys Hartland ', Cowslip scented, 10s. 6d.

' Bishop Mann ' was a vigorous early variety that might repay reintroduction from some Irish garden judging from the illustration in *The Garden*, July 22nd, 1899. Barr's 1884 list contained more than twenty forms classed as moschatus varieties, of which only four or five could be obtained to-day, two of which, pallidus praecox and ' W. P. Milner ', are not really white.

The majority of the older white Daffodils had weak constitutions, requiring care and specially favourable positions to keep them healthy. They were the fond gazelles of the poet rather than the nine-lived cats, like ' Mme. de Graaff ', ' Mrs. Ernest Krelage ', ' White Wax ', ' Beersheba ' and the other sturdy plants of to-day.

' Mme. de Graaff's ' opaque whiteness and well-balanced trumpet, with its fascinatingly rolled-back rim, gained a F.C.C. for it in 1887, and bulbs were sold at £5 a piece; now 2d. will buy a bulb. This reduction is not because the variety has gone out of favour, but rather because its vigour and freedom of increase have placed it within the reach of all.

' Peter Barr ', the first of the giant whites, was bought by a few enthusiasts at its first appearance at fifty guineas a bulb, and still fetches 2s. in spite of too short a stem for so large a flower.

More than a score of magnificent and vigorous white trumpets are offered now at prices ranging from 1s. for The Brodie's beautiful ' Trappist ' to £5 for his ' Askelon '.

' Trappist ' has an evenly rolled-back rim to a trumpet which is lemon yellow at first and matures to a pure white. ' Askelon ' does not entirely lose the tone of lemon in its bell-mouthed, perfectly balanced trumpet.

' Beersheba ' attracts the notice of all by its great size and glittering whiteness. It has achieved 5 inches in diameter on a stalk of 20 inches, coming close to ' Kantara,' the largest white Ajax, which can reach 5½ inches across. Its outline is unusual and very striking; the perianth segments have long points and clean-cut edges forming a six-rayed star, or two triangles. The trumpet is curiously narrow at the base, and widens gradually to the open mouth in a curve that recalls the outline of a Convolvulus flower.

Few people have yet realised the beauty of white Daffodils as cut flowers. A wide-mouthed glass vase should be filled with a bunch of twigs of Bog Myrtle, with unopened brown catkins for first choice, though Prunus Pissardii and its young brown leaves, or even bare twigs of Hawthorn, will do; seven ' Beersheba ' blooms should be scattered among the brown twigs, rather loosely; then five of one of the deep yellow Incomparabilis varieties such as ' Jubilant ', ' Havelock ' or ' St. Ives ' might be used as a contrast, three to be packed shoulder to shoulder towards the centre, one with shortened stalk to the left, and the other turning away towards the back on the right.

Such an arrangement ought to convert anyone to a belief in the value of white Daffodils. Closely bunched as packed for market they look cold, the beauty of their form is lost, and there is no glow of colour and play of reflected light, such as a tight bunch of ' King Alfred ' will provide.

' Eskimo ', ' White Knight ', ' Snowscape ', ' White Wax ' and ' White Emperor ' are some smaller flowers very good for the garden, pots or cutting.

VII

Bicolor Trumpet Daffodils

THIS IS Division I.*c* of the R.H.S. Classification.

N. Pseudo-Narcissus was the name Linnæus selected from those used by older writers under which in the First Edition of *Species Plantarum* he grouped all forms with solitary flowers and what he defined as campanulate nectaries equal in length to the petals. The comparative shape and dimensions of the nectary, or as we should say corona, seemed to him the chief distinguishing character. He added N. bicolor, minor and moschatus as additional species in the Second Edition.

Salisbury made his genus Ajax to include all trumpet forms, and was followed by Haworth and Herbert, using Pseudo-Narcissus solely as the specific name for our native plant and its varieties.

J. G. Baker returned to its use as a group name, and placed the Linnean species minor, bicolor and moschatus, as well as cyclamineus and major, under it as subspecies.

Thus we have been cumbered by the use of this rather unpleasant title for many trumpet forms that have little or no relationship to the small wild species.

Mr. Pugsley's recent *Monograph* should at any rate set us free from the use of this absurd group name, though his alternative ' vulgares ' is not particularly flattering.

Bauhin's *Pinax* quotes the French Edition of Dodoens *History of Plants* for the first use of Pseudonarcissus. That would be in 1557, and it occurs in Lyte's English translation of 1578 as Bastarde Narcissus. Lyte gives

Crowbels as another English name. Gerard wrote:
' The common yellow Daffodilly or Daffadowndilly
is so well knowne to all, that it needeth no description.' Unfortunately it is not so well known as
formerly, the spread of towns and cultivation having
exterminated it from many localities.

Clusius wrote in 1601 that it grew so abundantly in
meadows near London that in March countrywomen
gathered great quantities for sale, and in the district
commonly called ' Ceapside ' all shops were decorated
with it.

Its early flowering, coming ' before the Swallows
dare ', and its neat dwarf habit make it quite the best
for naturalising in grass and thin woodland where it
is not already found wild.

It seeds itself freely where the pods are allowed
to ripen, and does not lose its charm of slender stalk
and contrasting shades of yellow in the pale perianth
and darker trumpet, unless grown so near to larger
garden forms that it is affected by their pollen. Occasionally a white seedling appears, but hitherto these
have not been sufficiently vigorous to increase and be
distributed.

The variety sold as scoticus has paler, more spreading perianth segments and a more important trumpet
with spreading, serrated brim.

The plant well known in gardens as *N. princeps* is
supposed to be of Italian origin, but there is only
traditional evidence for this view.

It is well figured in Jordan's *Icones*, 357, as
N. Gayi of Henon, from a cultivated specimen of
unknown native locality. It resembles our Lent Lily,
except that it is about twice the size and has a relatively
shorter perianth tube, and like it flourishes and spreads
in meadows and orchards if it is allowed to seed.

It has been much grown for market, but has such
a flimsy substance that it lasts only a very short time

when cut. Self-sown seedlings vary considerably; some have perianth segments a good deal longer than the trumpet, producing an unpleasing, lop-eared effect.

Double forms have been known and listed, but seem to have disappeared.

N. Gayi has a remarkably strong scent, very much like the earthy or ivy-leaf odour that is unpleasant, if sniffed at too vigorously, in the old Double Daffodil; in Gayi there is a secondary odour like that of Almonds.

' Vanilla ', a variety raised by Van der Schoot in Holland, has this pleasant scent purified of the earthy tang. The name was given because this fragrance has a slight resemblance to that of vanilla. It is, however, more like the scent left in a chocolate box after the contents have vanished.

' Spring Glory ', another bicolor of Dutch origin, has a similarly pleasant scent; being easily forced and possessing fragrance, it will be found one of the most suitable varieties for growing in pots for house decoration.

The bicoloured Daffodils found so plentifully in the French Pyrenees are of a sturdier type than the Lent Lilies of the lower lands. They are very variable in form, and the best of them have widely expanded trumpets of a good strong yellow which in some is so deep that it approaches a light orange. This deep colouring frequently suffuses the tube, replacing the green which is found in the Lent Lilies. The perianth is very white, much more so than in N. Gayi.

Their chief value in a garden is their earliness, and on sunny banks they are among the first to open. Many years ago collected forms were listed as *N. nobilis* or variiformis. The latter would be a good and descriptive name for this variable clan, but except for catalogues and Parkinson's pyrenaeus variiformis has no authority behind it, and Pugsley refers them to N. nobilis Schultes.

The late Mr. James Allen, of Snowdrop fame,
collected good forms and named the best ' Allen's
Beauty '.   It is very early, a beautifully balanced flower
with a wide, white perianth and a shapely trumpet of
good yellow, but being dwarf and terribly niggardly
of its flowers is but little grown.   Judiciously crossed
it might help to add earliness to bicoloured trumpets.

Linnæus added several species in the Second Edition
of *Species Plantarum*, and of these *N. bicolor* is one.
There is a well-preserved specimen in his herbarium
from a plant grown in the Upsala Garden.   It still
shows distinctly that the perianth has wide overlapping
segments of lighter colouring than the slightly lobed
corona.   It is the N. albus calice flavo moscari odore
of Bauhin's *Pinax*.   There is a good picture of it in
t. 1187 of the *Botanical Magazine*, where Gawler
describes it as ' two-coloured, and not of a uniform
deep yellow ', and further on as almost white as to
the perianth.   The figure shows a rather buffish cream
perianth, called ' very pale sulphur-yellow ' by Baker,
but by Burbidge ' snowy white ', as shown in his Plate 6.

Mr. Pugsley states that the typical plant has almost
disappeared in gardens and is represented by two
rather distinct forms, grandis, a very useful late-flowering plant with nearly white perianth, and lorifolius,
which he shows to be the right name for the rugilobus
of gardens, which, however, is not the rugilobus of
Haworth.   N. lorifolius has a rather muddy, pale
yellow perianth very much like that in the *Bot. Mag.*
figure, and a strong scent with a dash of lemon in it,
which may be the moscari odore noted by Bauhin.

N. bicolor in one of its forms produced the first
great break in the way of seedlings.   In the hands of
John Horsefield[1] it gave about 1845 N . Horsfieldii,
one of the most popular kinds for forcing and massing

[1] Horsefield spelt his name with a central e, but it was omitted
in the name under which the plant was published.

over a long period. Unfortunately, being much affected by Fusarium, it is now almost discarded by growers. Its clear contrast of white perianth and yellow trumpet is well shown in Moon's beautiful plate in *The Garden* for September 8th, 1888.

Later on, in the sixties, William Backhouse of St. John's, near Wolsingham, raised ' Empress '. Being larger, late-flowering and of very robust constitution, it has taken the place of Horsfieldii. ' Emperor ' and ' Empress ' are stated to have been raised from crosses between N. bicolor and N. Pseudo-Narcissus. ' Emperor ' is so much like the old rugilobus of gardens in colouring that it seems likely this was its seed parent. Both were figured in vol. viii. of the *Floral Magazine* in 1869 by James Andrews with leaves that would fit an Antholyza, and flowers enlarged to such a size as to make them appallingly ugly. Burbidge's Pl. 9 is not much better, but that in *The Garden* for September 15th, 1883, is a truthful portrait.

The engraving of ' Emperor ' by Kohl in *The Garden*, December 3rd, 1892, from a photograph, is a good piece of work, but accentuates the imperial wrinkles and rugosities somewhat unkindly. Though Cromwell wished his warts to appear in his portrait, he would have had cause for complaint had they been emphasised to a similar extent.

N. abscissus as a name stands to the credit of Schultes, who was the first to use this combination in 1830. The specific name was used earlier by Haworth in conjunction with Ajax. Gay called the plant A. muticus in 1860, and that specific name had been in general use until Mr. Pugsley's monograph restored the older name.

Both names refer to the curiously abrupt, straight edge of the corona, which Parkinson called the ' clipt trunke ' (' tubo quasi abscisso ') . . . ' not crumpled or turned up as most of the other are, and that the brimmes or edges of the flower is as if it had been clipt off or cut even '.

It is a bicolor of strongly contrasted white perianth and yellow, cylindrical trumpet, and quite unmistakable owing to the ' clipt ' appearance of its mouth. It occurs in the Pyrenees in great quantities, and mostly unmixed with other trumpet forms; and as it does not vary a great deal it is rather an uninteresting plant to meet with, except where it grows among N. poeticus, and specimens of their hybrid offspring, N. Bernardii, may be found. It covers the hillside in the Val d'Esquierry, growing among that other dull and dominating plant Asphodelus subalpinus.

In the garden it flowers late and lasts long even when the weather has become too warm for other forms. N. grandis resembles it slightly in form and much in its lateness, suggesting abscissus as one parent.

N. parviflorus (Jord.) Pugsley. In his Pl. 366, Jordan figured a curious, small-flowered, bicoloured form found near Gèdres in the Pyrenees as Ajax parviflorus. It is rather tall, with a slightly twisted perianth and a ridiculously narrow but lengthy corona with straight margin. It is clearly a depauperated form of N. abscissus, and so ugly that we may hope it will never be introduced to cultivation.

For garden and cutting the bicolor trumpets can be divided into those with deep yellow trumpets, for example ' Duke of Bedford ', as large a flower as is needed, to my thinking, and ' Empress ' and ' Victoria ', the well-known market favourites. The other class shows less contrast between the white or cream perianth and the yellow or lemon of the trumpet. ' Florence Pearson ', so little removed from a white, would represent that end of the scale, and ' Weardale Perfection ' in cream and lemon should come halfway up to ' Boswin ' and ' Bonython ', two good earlies with white perianth and lemon trumpets.

In the first class is the old variety 'Coronet', of medium size, and a trumpet formed on the lines of maximus standing out of a prettily twisted white perianth. Its form is well shown in 'Gardening Illustrated', September 2nd, 1911.

Very few good bicolors with deep yellow trumpets have been raised lately, so 'Duke of Bedford' still holds its own as a fine variety. 'Effective' and 'Jack Spratt', of Mr. Guy Wilson's raising, 'Rosemorran Giant', 'Dinton Giant' and 'Mrs. John Hoog' are fairly new and distinctly eminent.

Those with what compilers of lists call lemon, primrose, or soft yellow trumpets have been produced freely, and many of them are singularly beautiful in form and texture.

The Brodie has given us 'Quartz', a very refined flower with smooth, overlapping perianth segments and an evenly toothed, reflexed margin to the trumpet; a fine show flower and of a good medium height for growing in pots.

'Carmel' and 'Halfa', two more from The Brodie, have similarly recurved rims. 'Sincerity' is still too scarce for ordinary folk to order in quantity, and so beautiful that it is unlikely to cheapen rapidly.

'Bonython' flowers very early and is tall and sturdy, and with its companion 'Boswin' provides the first blooms of lemon yellow and white trumpets.

'Moira O'Neil' and 'Manna' are good forms available now, but most people must wait a bit longer for such glories as 'Gregalloch', 'Tapin' and 'Queen of Ulster'.

Two interesting varieties with a slight flush of rose-pink in the trumpet are 'Jersey Cream' from The Brodie and 'Rosary' from Mr. Engleheart.

VIII

SMALL-FLOWERED AND DOUBLE TRUMPETS

FOR GARDEN purposes the small-flowered group can
be defined as having flowers less than 2 inches in
length from ovary to rim of trumpet. Mr. Pugsley in
his masterly *Monograph* makes them Series I. Minores
of his Section II. Pseudo-Narcissus, defined as ' Flowers
small or very small, Yellow or bicoloured, with flowering pedicel not deflexed or very short '. In either case
all the plants brought together flower early, and those
of authenticated wild origin are Spanish. Some have
been garden favourites for at least two hundred years,
and have received so many names that bewildering
confusion has resulted.

We are greatly indebted to Mr. Pugsley for his
careful work in collecting and arranging the facts
relating to these small plants, though his conclusions
may force us to use unfamiliar names for them.

The forms most frequently met with may be distinguished thus:

A. Corona with convex outline constricted below the
   eighteen-toothed mouth: N. asturiensis (minimus of gardens).

B. Corona with nearly straight outline.

   (1) Leaves narrow, flowers nearly concolorous.
   × Scape 6 to 8 inches, perianth segments
   separated by a space at their base:

   N. minor.

   × × Scape shorter, 2 to 4 inches, perianth
   segments overlapping at base:

   N. pumilus (nanus of gardens).

79

(2) Leaves broad, flowers bicoloured, perianth
segments broad, ovate:
N. nanus (lobularis of gardens).

N. asturiensis Jordan (*N. minimus* of gardens).   This
minute plant has several distinct features which in-
dicate specific rank.   The slender scape is nearly
cylindrical and very evenly ribbed.   Where ovary and
tube join, there is a distinct waist due to the convex
outline of the cup-shaped perianth tube.   This convex outline continues above the insertion of the perianth, reducing the diameter of the corona to a conspicuous constriction above which the mouth widens
out into a regularly toothed rim which is generally
rolled outwards.

The spathe remains brilliantly green for a longer
period after the flower is open than in any other dwarf
form, and the filaments of all the stamens are inserted
right at the base of the tube.

It is generally concolorous in perianth and corona,
and of a pure, bright yellow, though seedlings show
slight variations of colouring.

C. de Pas gives a figure in his division Hyems 8
as N. pumilus, which as to the flower I believe resembles this plant.   The leaves are too broad, but
are so obviously added without any regard to their
manner of growth that they may not belong to it.

The most important figure is Jordan's, in his *Icones
ad Floram Europae*, vol. iii., 4, showing five specimens.
From this work the name asturiensis is taken, and if
Haworth's Ajax minimus of his *Monograph* can be
proved to have been meant for some other plant,
Jordan's name must be accepted, though published
as late as 1903.

As minimus it has long been a favourite in gardens,
and pleases everyone in that it is the earliest to flower
as well as the smallest Trumpet Daffodil in cultivation.

It is still collected in Spain and Portugal and is plentiful in many nurseries, not difficult to grow, and will sow itself freely if the seedpods can be protected. Some tiresome inhabitants of gardens make a hole in plump pods and devour the seeds before their coat has hardened. I suspect linnets as the chief offenders.

In short grass or in pans for the Alpine House, as well as in the lower ground of the Rock Garden, it is one of the best bulbous plants in flower at the end of the Winter.

Herbert's quaint little figures of pumilus and cuneiflorus on Pl. 43 of his *Amaryllidaceae* drawn from specimens in Banks's herbarium are apparently minute forms of this.

Burbidge's Pl. 5 B is a good figure, and one of the best is his drawing of a whole plant in *The Garden*, p. 287 of vol. xxiii., 1883. The lowest flower on p. 272 of vol. xxv., 1884, is not good, though drawn by Burbidge. Good photographs of the habit of the plant are reproduced in Mr. Calvert's *Daffodil Growing*, p. 214, and *Gardening Illustrated*, December 5th, 1931, p. 738. A photograph reproduced in *The Garden* for April 21st, 1900, p. 296, contains minor and minimus, and the central flower shows very clearly the characteristic form of the corona and the manner in which each of its six indistinctly divided lobes is again cut up into three teeth, forming a recurved frill of eighteen nearly equal points.

N. minor was described by Linnæus in the Second Edition of *Species Plantarum*. He distinguishes it as having an obconic, crispate, six-lobed corona and lanceolate segments in contrast with the campanulate corona of Pseudo-Narcissus. In a further note he describes it as one-third the size in all its parts, the scape scarcely striated, the flower nodding, the segments separated from one another at the base, lanceolate, straight, not oblique or ovate, and the spathe green.

6

His herbarium specimen shows a flower standing away from the distinctly striated scape at an obtuse angle.

He cites Clusius's Ps.-N. minor hispanicus of the *Historia*, p. 165. The figure to this shows a nodding flower with distinctly convex swollen tube and evenly toothed margin to the corona, that would better represent N. asturiensis, as also would the scarcely striated scape and green spathe of Linnæus's description.

It is unlikely that Linnæus knew many of these dwarf Narcissi in a living state, and it would be in accordance with his usual practice to intend that a somewhat generalised description and one specimen should include closely related forms described by earlier authors.

Nothing exactly like his type specimen has yet been found in a wild state. Dr. Giuseppi collected a small plant on the Serro da Estrella, one of the localities given in Coutinho's *Flora of Portugal* for N. minor. I have only seen one flower of this. It resembles Linnæus's type in perianth segments and has the short pedicel of the t. 6 of the *Botanical Magazine*.

Seedlings of these small forms vary considerably where they sow themselves in gardens; therefore J. G. Baker had good reasons for arranging them as no more than varieties of a subspecies minor of Pseudo-Narcissus.

The cultivated form that comes nearest to the minor of Linnæus is an old garden plant much grown in Ireland. It is remarkably slender, almost self yellow, the segments slightly twisted, narrow and with a distinct space between each of them at their bases; the mouth of the corona is deeply six-lobed, and each lobe is divided into three large teeth with folded-back edges.

Its characters are clearly shown by the two larger flowers in a photograph illustrating an article by Mr. Engleheart in *The Garden* for April 21st, 1900,

p. 296. Burbidge's figures mostly show it with a somewhat convex tube, like that of asturiensis. This is noticeable in Pl. 5 of his monograph and also in his drawing on p. 272 of *The Garden*, vol. xxv., 1884. The group of growing plants, in Mr. Calvert's Pl. 46, shows a form with wide perianth segments overlapping at their base, resembling the flower of N. nanus Spach. A white form was grown in Ireland and may still exist there, though it was difficult to grow in England and died out under my care.

Fig. 3 on p. 9 of Hartland's *Original Little Book of Daffodils* of 1887 is called White minor, but under N. lobularis Hartland wrote: ' White minor and Little Nell (also figured in the group) should fit into this type and not into the minor or nanus section.' This is borne out by the flower shown in Moon's beautiful painting of White Daffodils in *The Garden*, vol. xxxviii., July 26th, 1890. In the text to this plate Mr. Engleheart wrote: ' The rarest and most shapely is the little " White minor " shown towards the middle of the plate and lowest down; it has been discovered in but one or two Irish Gardens and is but a shy flowerer when found.'

N. minor has been accused of producing some double-flowered forms. All that I have seen appear too stout and heavy to claim such a slender parent.

The strange little plant known as ' Rip van Winkle ' was considered a seedling of minor by Hartland, but Burbidge thought it more likely a double of Pseudo-Narcissus and figured and described it in *The Garden*, vol. xxvii., p. 143, in 1885. Its chief feature consists of the repeated whorls of perianth segments with narrow points bent at their tips like crochet hooks which surround the central coronal divisions.

N. *pumilus* is the name Mr. Pugsley selected for the plant so long known as *N. nanus* in gardens.

The name pumilus was used by Salisbury in 1796 in his *Prodromus* and afterwards changed to Ajax cuneiflorus in the *Transactions of the Horticultural Society* in 1812. It had been used by C. de Pas in 1614 for a figure which I consider represents the flower of N. asturiensis if, as is not impossible, the leaves were drawn from those of some other form.

Mr. Pugsley considers Haworth's Ajax minimus a smaller variety of N. minor. Haworth connects it with Curtis's N. minor, Fig. 6 of the *Botanical Magazine*, and describes it as shown there with imbricated perianth segments and spreading leaves and the six lobes of the corona much frilled. He also cites Parkinson's vile Fig. 3 on p. 107 and his description of the flower touching the ground.

The imbricated segments and spreading leaves seem to me to connect it with the subject of t. 198 of Sweet's *British Flower Garden*, Series II., which Mr. Pugsley recognises as N. pumilus of Salisbury. Such a plant is grown in gardens as N. nanus and is remarkable for the curious way in which the unopened flower buds in their long green spathes rest upon the ground. No other Daffodil resembles it in this habit, and it must surely be Parkinson's Least Spanish yellow of which ' Every flower standeth upon a small and short foote-stalk, scarce rising above the ground, so that his nose, for the most part, doth lye or touch the ground '.

A few days after the flowers open, the stalk lengthens and carries them up four or more inches. Unfortunately slugs frequently find the corona within reach and devour it before it can be lifted to safety. Slugs seldom climb the scape but greedily devour Daffodil flowers beaten down to the ground by frost or rain.

This form is a strong grower and increases well, and is the better for frequent replanting. When crowded the flowers are small as in Curtis's figure and the leaves are forced to stand upright; when well spaced the leaves

spread as shown by Curtis and Sweet and the flowers
are large. It seeds freely, but produces mongrel
offspring resembling the Lent Lily, pallidiflorus and
others, but generally recognisable by the short scape
and six-lobed corona.

The black and white Fig. 646 in Nicholson's *Dictionary* is good and shows the spreading habit of the
leaves. It is there called N. Ps.-N. minor nanus.

The Fringed Narcissus of Hill's *Eden* has been
glorified by Mr. Pugsley into the var. fimbriatus of
N. pumilus with a reproduction of Hill's figure. I
cannot regard it as anything but a very bad drawing
of no greater botanical value than those in the work
of the same period known as *Bowles's Florist*. Both the
single and double Daffodil therein and other Narcissi of
that work are quite impossible in form, with leaves curled
and waved in the same manner as in Hill's figure, and
may have been drawn by the same untruthful artist.

N. lobularis of gardens seems to have no right to
that name. It was coined by Haworth for what he
called the Tenby six-lobed Daffodil and described as
yellow in perianth and corona, whereas the plant in
question is bicolorous. Mr. Pugsley regards it as the
N. nanus of Spach's *Hist. Nat. de Végétaux*, XII.,
1846, and Ajax nanus of Haworth's monograph, 1831.
In his *Revisio* of 1819, Haworth made it Ajax minor
var. conspicuus, though he had not then seen its flower,
only the tall leaves as it grew in the Horticultural
Society's Garden in London, having been obtained
from a Dutch Garden as N. major.

Barr obtained a plant from Holland as N. minor
and in 1873 sent a flower to Kew, where the name
lobularis was applied to it and has been in use in
gardens ever since. In those days a Latin name
was dealt out to every slight variation found in gardens,
and it was only in 1884 that the Daffodil Conference
held by the Royal Horticultural Society resolved that

' Garden varieties of Narcissi, whether known hybrids or natural seedlings, should be named or numbered in the manner adopted by Florists, and not in the manner adopted by the Botanists '.

The plant is still grown by Messrs. Barr and has all the appearance of a garden-raised seedling, with a bicoloured Trumpet as one parent, and it would be better to use an English name for it.

It lacks the elegance and charm of other early dwarf forms, its two shades of yellow are rather dull and the leaves so broad that it looks like a dwarfed condition of a large plant.

Mr. Pugsley's Fig. 12, a photograph of the specimen in the Fielding herbarium at Oxford, could not be bettered to represent the characters of the plant.

A double-flowered plant is known as lobularis flore pleno. The flowers are so closely packed with successive whorls of contorted portions of perianth and corona that they appear dumpy and untidy and more curious than beautiful.

The Ajax section has produced several double varieties, but except the old Double Daffodil, the white double so long known as N. cernuus fl. pl. now connected with moschatus, and perhaps the latest development, ' Holland's Glory ', a supposed sport from ' Emperor ', none are so good as the double forms of incomparabilis. This is possibly due to the extra length of the coronal segments in Ajax interfering with the symmetry of the succeeding whorls.

Some double forms of Ajax vary greatly from season to season, and no bulb can be relied upon to present a similar form in two consecutive years. In these varieties the trumpet may be perfectly formed as in the normal single flower, but filled up with repeated whorls of perianth segments and portions of corona; or, at the other extreme, the corona may be split into many sections and repeated in several whorls, mixed irregularly among variously sized and shaped perianth pieces. The flowers are then exceedingly variable and generally have a confused and untidy appearance not so pleasing as in those with unsplit coronas.

These two extremes and numerous intermediate forms may be noticed in any garden where the old Double Daffodil is plentiful; and bulbs selected for the sake of an especially pleasing form may never again produce it, and are quite likely to bear flowers of the worst possible shape in some seasons.

The origin of this common Double Daffodil is as much a mystery as that of wheat, the potato and many of our most useful plants and domestic animals. No single-flowered form that would match it in colour and texture is now known, though the double form is scattered all over the temperate regions and frequently occurs as a naturalised plant in meadows and out of the way places, as a remnant of some long vanished garden ground. I received bulbs of it collected in wild ground near Salonica.

Its first appearance in England is that chronicled by Parkinson, who tells in the *Paradisus* that Vincent Sion, a Fleming, living in London, cherished it in his garden for many years before it flowered in the year 1620. He thought that John de Frauqueville might have given him the bulb, but that worthy disclaimed the honour, never having seen the like before. Before his death Van Sion gave bulbs to George Wilmer of Stratford Bowe, and also to Parkinson, who seems somewhat aggrieved that Wilmer 'would needes appropriate it to himselfe, as if he were the first founder thereof, and call it by his own name Wilmer's double Daffodil, which since hath so continued '.

It was not the only name it was to bear, for Haworth invented an Ajax Telamon (named after the father of Ajax), but afterwards changed the name to Telamonius. He provided a very poor description for it, and it is hopeless to attempt to recognise any single-flowered form now grown, as his 'long-flowered' Ajax.   He regarded it as the single form of two doubles, for the first of which, grandiplenus, the great double, he cites Parkinson's Fig. 7 on p. 101, called there Master Wilmer's Great Double Daffodill.   Therefore the name, Telamonius plenus, has been widely used. As there is only Haworth's word for connecting it with the intangible Telamonius, it is better to call it by the garden name Van Sion, and to give honour to whom, according to Parkinson, honour is due.

Parkinson calls his No. 5 ' Gerrard's Double Daffodil ', and declares that Gerard found it in a poor woman's garden in the West Parts of England, and that it grew wild in the Isle of Wight.   Now Gerard only mentioned one double form and said that he received it from Robinus of Paris.   However, a small double form, though it is very scarce, still exists in a garden or two and appears to be a double form of the wild Lent Lily.

Parkinson's No. 1, ' John Tradescant, his great Rose Daffodil ', is well figured by Burbidge on Pl. 11 as N. Ps.-N. grandiplenus.   Haworth called it var. E. plenissimus (having used grandiplenus for his double Telamonius).   So if anyone still grows this heavy-headed, overloaded double flower it would be safest to call it Tradescant's Daffodil.   When I grew it I found that it varied, as other double trumpets will, from season to season; but it was always a clumsy and ugly flower.

The most elaborately doubled form of this shows traces of fasciation, and as figured in Barr's *Ye Narcissus*, in 1884, drawn by Burbidge, the central portion is made up of about ten distinct axes of growth closely packed into a round head.   This condition must be the foundation of the ludicrous figure in Rudbeck's *Campi Elysii*, xiv., p. 81, as N. luteus tubo diviso. It looks like a Chrysanthemum with four blossoms of an Auricula stuck about among the florets.

N. eystettensis, generally placed with Trumpet varieties and otherwise known as capax plenus or Queen Anne's Double Daffodil, is another plant of mysterious origin.

It stands alone in possessing several remarkable characters. These are, the absence of perianth tube and corona; the arrangement of the perianth segments in six opposite whorls, succeeding segments being placed exactly above one below to form a perfect star of six points; and the pale creamy-yellow colouring of the whole flower.

The rather poor woodcut used by Clusius on p. 165 of his *Historia* seems intended for this. His description states that it was grown in Belgian gardens, the calyx (meaning corona) was lacking in its centre and was replaced by many altogether similar pale leaves. He called it Pseudonarcissus pleno flore.

In the Second Appendix he provided a different figure and description for a double Pseudo-Narcissus fl. pl. sent to him by Venerius from the Pyrenees, a true Trumpet form with twelve perianth segments and three coronas one within the other.

Lobel, and Johnson in his Edition of Gerard, used Clusius's block showing the starry flower; Tabernaemontanus used an older one with wider leaves but the star-shaped flower quite recognisable. Gerard used this older block for the double form he received from Robinus of Paris. Their descriptions throw no light upon the origin of the plant.

Parkinson calls it the Lesser French Double Daffodil, Ps.-N. Gallicus minor flore pleno, to distinguish it from his greater kind which seems to be N. moschatus fl. pl. He describes it as ' of a pale yellow or lemon colour, consisting of six rowes of leaves, every rowe growing smaller then other unto the middle and so set or placed that every leafe of the flower doth stand directly almost in all, one upon or before another unto the middle . . . and hath no trunke '.

He states that it grew plentifully about Orleans. His figure, No. 4 on p. 107, is good, being a pretty fair copy of the very beautiful one No. 20 in the *Theatrum Florae*. Parkinson had doubts about its being a Bastard Daffodil. Herbert guessed it was connected with N. minor, but had not seen a flower.

Another excellent figure is that drawn and engraved by Nicholas Robert for Dodart's *Mémoires pour servir à l'histoire des plantes*, a rare work published in Paris between 1675 and 1681. Pl. 282 of the copy in the Lindley Library represents N. sylvestris and contains a single-flowered plant which is N. Pseudo-Narcissus, and also a double-flowered one which is eystettensis but named N. sylvestris multiplex, Narcisse de Goumas. This may be Goumois, a small French town near Besançon. This beautifully drawn figure corroborates the belief set forth in the seventeenth century that eystettensis was a double form of Pseudo-Narcissus and originated in France.

Haworth makes it a double form of his Assaracus capax, a species he founded on N. calathinus of De Candolle figured in *Les Liliacées*, which is N. triandrus var. calathinus.

I believe he is nearest to the truth, for Mr. Van de Weyer raised a form very much like it by placing pollen of 'Van Sion' on N. triandrus. The perianth segments in this are arranged for the most part as in eystettensis, but a minute section of coronal origin appears here and there; the perianth tube is rather longer, and the flower more pendent. So it seems likely that Queen Anne's Daffodil may be a garden hybrid of the six-teenth century with triandrus as one parent and some double-flowered form for the other.

It should not be confused with Queen Anne's Jonquil, the double-flowered N. Jonquilla, nor does it seem right to call either of these plants of a much earlier date after the eighteenth-century Queen.

IX

INCOMPARABILIS

DIVISION II. of the R.H.S. Classification covers forms with cup or crown not less than one-third, but less than equal to, the length of the perianth segments. This is divided into (*a*) yellow shades and (*b*) bicolor varieties with white or whitish perianth, and both can be with or without red colouring in the cup. Botanically they are classed under *N. incomparabilis*—the name given by Miller in the Gardeners' Dictionary. In the Eighth Edition (1768) it is spelt incomparibilis, but Parkinson gave the accepted spelling and appears to have been the first to use it.

It was the N. omnium maximus of Crispin de Pas's beautiful figure in the *Hortus Floridus* of 1614, which he said was sent to Christian Porretus of Leyden under the French name nompareille.

Parkinson wrote that it was not so large as the Great Spanish bastard Daffodil and ' therefore this name was given but relatively, we may call it in English The Great None Such, The Incomparable or the Great Peerlesse Daffodil—and because this name Nompareille is grown currant by custom, I know not well how to alter it '. Would that we did call it the Peerless, if that would prevent the frequent use of the hideous word ' incomps ' which is almost as horrible as ' mums ' for Chrysanthemum, the Golden Flower.

Salisbury founded the genus Queltia for these long-cupped plants in honour of Nicholas le Quelt, who collected the first of them above Luchon. Herbert retained Queltia, adding as an English name Mock-Narcissus, and dubbed the principal species Q. foetida,

91

writing ' flower stinking in all that I have seen ', with
five varieties of which No. 1 is incomparabilis. Even
' incomp ' is better than a translation of foetida for this
group.

The slender form figured in t. 121 of the *Botanical
Magazine* is generally considered the type, but differs
greatly from the massive flower shown by de Pas and
Parkinson and the *Theatrum Florae*, which is more like
' Sir Watkin '.

All forms of N. incomparabilis are undoubtedly
hybrids between Ajax and poeticus and can be raised
with ease in gardens. The form of this cross named
N. Bernardii occurs in the Pyrenees where the two
grow together, but only as scattered plants, and
wherever colonies of one form only are found in Italy
and France they are probably escapes from cultivation,
as in the case of N. odorus.

In cultivation incomparabilis sported freely in early
times, producing doubles that were garden favourites
in the seventeenth century and are still grown where
gardeners are wise enough to value old plants of
reliably vigorous constitution. Such are the old-
fashioned ' Butter and Eggs ', of two shades of yellow;
' Eggs and Bacon ' or ' Orange Phœnix ', with perianth
segments of sulphury white and coronal segments of
deep orange; ' Codlings and Cream ' or ' Sulphur
Phœnix ', creamy white and the coronal fragments
small and almost hidden at the base of the perianth.
These held first place as the garden favourites of this
division until the appearance of ' Sir Watkin ' in
1884.

F. W. Burbidge wrote the text accompanying
Moon's beautiful coloured plate in *The Garden*,
vol. xxviii., 1885. ' The Welsh Peerless ', he says,
' is one of those comet or meteor-like flowers which
all at once flash on the flower-loving public from
whence no one appears to know.' It resembles Ate's

I   Narcissus "Beersheba"

'. . . attracts the attention of all by its great size and glittering
whiteness . . . the trumpet is curiously narrow at the base, and widens
gradually to the open mouth in a curve that recalls the outline of a
convolvulus flower.'

2   Narcissus asturiensis
'It has long been a favourite in gardens, and pleases everyone in that it is the earliest to flower as well as the smallest Trumpet Daffodil in cultivation.'

3   Narcissus "Rip Van Winkle"
'The strange little plant known as "Rip Van Winkle" . . . Its chief
feature consists of the repeated whorls of perianth segments with
narrow points bent at their tips like crochet hooks.'

4   Narcissus telamonius plenus
'The origin of this common Double Daffodil is as much a mystery as
that of wheat, the potato and many of our most useful plants and
domestic animals.'

5   Narcissus "Mrs R. O. Backhouse"
'So-called 'pink-cupped' varieties have been much admired. The late
Mrs R. O. Backhouse raised the first. It bears her honoured name and
was shown in 1923 . . . it is a wonderful flower.'

6   Narcissus cyclamineus

'The drifts of its gay flowers rising from green moss or thin grass as
may be seen at Wisley should inspire any gardener who has patience
and a similar situation to plant and sow and watch over cyclamineus,
until he gains a corresponding reward.'

7   Narcissus juncifolius

'It colours meadowland, as buttercups do with us, in some parts of the Pyrenees . . . with its brilliantly yellow well-formed flowers, delicious scent and neat habit it is very desirable for a rock garden, or for pans in the alpine house.'

8   NARCISSUS CANALICULATUS
'flowers later than its near relations and is a charming dwarf plant for a
sheltered nook in a rock.'

9 NARCISSUS "PAPERWHITE"
'It is an old garden plant which has been largely cultivated in Italy for centuries . . . it is always the first Narcissus to appear in the markets, providing a welcome suggestion of Spring and a change from the Chrysanthemums that have reigned supreme for the last three months.'

10   Narcissus "Geranium"
'By using a better form of poeticus as one parent still larger forms have
been raised . . . "Geranium" of Van der Schoot has the largest flowers
of any.'

11   N ARCISSUS SEROTINUS
'This minute plant is the most widely spread of the Autumn-flowering
species, being found in Southern Europe from Portugal to Greece,
along the Mediterranean region of North Africa and in Palestine.'

'The great variability of Narcissus bulbocodium in size, form and
coloration makes it difficult to define any form as a distinct variety.'

13   NARCISSUS BULBOCODIUM CITRINUS
'In England (it) will grow in moist ground that is not waterlogged, but
better still in cool, mossy woodland and grassy slopes as at Wisley,
where it sows itself freely and varies endlessly. . .'

14   N A R C I S S U S   C A N T A B R I C U S

'. . . a veritable gem for the Alpine House and for growing in pans.
The pure white flowers are beautifully crystalline when they are
young and equally admirable when the corona becomes thinner . . .'

15   NARCISSUS "DICK TURPIN"

'. . . combines an ivory-white perianth with a perfectly flat deep red corona slightly in the centre.'.

NARCISSUS OBVALLARIS
'I regard Narcissus obvallaris as the most perfect in proportion and
texture of any deep yellow trumpet . . .'

17   Narcissus alpestris
Narcissus moschatus fl.pl.

Narcissus "Fortune"
'a surprise for the Daffodil world occurred when Mr. Walter T. Ware
exhibited 'Fortune' at Birmingham in 1915. Nothing of its size then
possessed such a depth of orange coloration in the corona.'

19   N ARCISSUS "F OLLY"
'. . . the peculiar charm of its brilliancy, gaiety and refinement.'

20   N A R C I S S U S "M A R Y C O P E L A N D"

'. . . perhaps the best of the Incomparabilis doubles.'

NARCISSUS "SACRIFICE"
'the corona is . . . uniform in colour and a brilliant orange-red.'

22   N a r c i s s u s   "W h i t e   N i l e"
'For perfection of form, substance and whiteness . . . 'White Nile' is
hard to beat, and being a free increaser will pay a good dividend.'

23   Narcissus "Niphetos"

'. . . the most perfect for form, poise, purity of white in the perianth
and a delicate tint of primrose in the young crown . . .'

NARCISSUS TAZETTA
NARCISSUS TRIANDUS GANYMEDIOIDES.

25   Narcissus triandus: var. calathinus;
var. concolor; var. albus; var. aurantiacus
'. . . Every variety of triandus is beautiful in shape and graceful
in habit.'

NARCISSUS "DAWN"

'. . . my favourite Daffodil, both for cutting and planting on ledges of the rock garden.'

27   NARCISSUS "SILVER CHIMES"

'. . . another plant of outstanding refinement and charm . . . a citron
tint as clear as the light of an evening sky.'

28   N a r c i s s u s   "B e r y l"
'. . . of medium cadmium yellow for the main colour, but broadly
edged with orange inside and out.'

NARCISSUS SCABERULUS. NARCISSUS
JUNCIFOLIUS. NARCISSUS WATIERI.

30 Narcissus "Trevithian". Narcissus "Hesla"

31   Narcissus "Sarchedon"

'. . . excellent for forcing and a good, all-round garden plant.'

32 Narcissus serotinus; Narcissus dubius;
Narcissus viridiflorus;
Narcissus elegans

Apple in the many claims for the honour of its discovery that were put forward, and to this day it remains
something of a mystery. One version runs that it
appeared in a Box edging, another that Welsh hillsides blazed with its gold, yet another that Captain
Byers brought it from Bideford to Pendyffrin in Wales,
where the bulbs increased and found their way into
neighbouring gardens.

The authentic and least romantic account states that
Mr. Pickstone found it in a garden near Dinas where he
went to live in 1868. He took bulbs with him when
he left Dinas, and after he settled in Flintshire sent
cut flowers to the Manchester Market. There Mr.
Dickson of Chester noticed them, and a boxful of
flowers was sent to the Narcissus Conference in
London in 1884. A week later a further consign-
ment received the F.C.C. of the R.H.S. under the
name of N. incomparabilis ' James Dickson '. At
Mr. Pickstone's request it was changed to ' Sir Watkin '
in memory of the late Sir W. W. Wynne.

This, however, throws no light on its origin. Is it
a survival of the omnium maximus of Pl. 19 in the
Theatrum Florae or perhaps a seedling from it with
another dose of Ajax? Burbidge decided against its
identity with the old figures, but the variations they
show may be greatly due to their draughtsmen and the
specimens before them.

It is said that the strain is wearing out and the
' Sir Watkin ' of the present day is losing vigour
and size; this may be due to the fact that it is no
longer a first favourite as a novelty, and less care
is bestowed upon it in ordinary gardens. Where
stocks have been carefully selected for propagation,
bulbs producing grand flowers are still procurable.

Another surprise for the Daffodil World occurred
when Mr. Walter T. Ware exhibited ' Fortune ' at
Birmingham in 1915. Nothing of its size then pos-

sessed such a depth of orange coloration in the
corona. Mr. Engleheart's 'Helios', which received
an A.M. in 1912, was the nearest approach to this
gorgeous giant. Here again many opinions have been
expressed as to the parentage. Was it one of the great
yellow trumpets such as maximus, 'King Alfred'
or 'M. J. Berkeley' as seed bearer, influenced by
a red-cupped incomparabilis, or, as has been stated,
from pollen of 'Sir Watkin' on the early-flowering
'Blackwell'? The last would account for 'Fortune's'
earliness, but does not seem likely to have produced
such size and substance.

It has proved one of the most sensational and successful seedlings of recent times. Ten years after its
first appearance it could not be purchased for less than
£25 a bulb, although it increases freely. It received
the F.C.C. in London in 1924 and has always stood
out as one of the most remarkable among early-
flowering varieties. In the hands of The Brodie of
Brodie it has fathered and mothered a numerous and
distinguished progeny, and will doubtless become a
grand garden plant and be particularly good for cutting, lasting well and retaining its colour when not
exposed to the trying weather generally met with at
its season of flowering. That, however, will not be
before it can go off the gold standard and be put
in circulation on a silver basis.

It is interesting for those old enough to do so to
recall the incomparabilis varieties grown in their
gardens when Leeds's seedlings were among the
novelties available. 'Cynosure' and 'Frank Miles'
with their starry perianth, and 'Princess Mary' with
brighter colouring in the cup and of better substance
and form, were thought much of in the eighties of
last century, but have either disappeared or are
relegated to the grass, to make way for their betters.
Even 'Sir Watkin' looks dull in colour and rough in

form beside the brilliantly clear yellow forms with wide, well-proportioned cups of the present day.

We may find many such among Lanarth seedlings. ' St. Ives ' stands out as one of the deepest in colour, has a round cup and tall stalk, flowers early and lasts well when cut, a magnificent garden plant. ' Arundel ' is rather larger, 4 inches in diameter, of a King Alfred yellow throughout. ' Havelock ' is larger still, having another ½ inch added to its diameter. The cup is deeper in colour than the perianth, the outer segments are set back and the inner a little forward, giving it a bold, pleasing outline.

' Jubilant ' is another large, brilliantly yellow self, very good in the garden and on the show bench. ' Carlton ' and ' Nimrod ' have wide cups with frilled edges; they are a pair of twins of soft, young duckling yellow very difficult to distinguish from one another except by those who know them well. ' Penbeagle ' has a wide rim to the cup beautifully lobed and rolled outwards. ' Golden Ingot ' and ' Golden Pedestal ', of Irish birth, have both won awards as exhibition varieties.

' Butter Bowl ' from Northern Ireland is distinct from the foregoing in having more pointed segments and a more open cup than ' Havelock ' which it resembles as to colour; it is a beautifully proportioned flower of shorter stature. ' Hopeful ' is a handsome flower of regular form and good proportion.

The yellows with red cups are among the most brilliant and striking (which is better than saying gaudy) varieties that catch everyone's eye in the groups at shows. At present it is asking too much of them to retain the same fiery brilliance in the garden without shading from frost and sunburn. Their forerunners ' C. J. Backhouse ', ' Blackwell ' and ' Gloria Mundi ' raised by Henry Backhouse are seldom seen now, but the last of these achieved a fairly wide distribution at the price of £5 a bulb in the Diamond Jubilee year. They were unreliable for colour, being affected by seasonal influences, and their importance has become chiefly historical. However, it would be a pity if these links in the chain of development are allowed to disappear altogether. Red in the cup is entirely due to inheritance from N. poeticus poetarum, another plant formerly prized and now neglected, if not lost, in most gardens.

'Aabenraa', raised by Mr. P. D. Williams and shown by Mr. Richardson, deserves first mention, not only because it lost the race for premier place in the Classified List by so short a neck as its third vowel, but it is a well-formed flower with much red colouring in its deep orange cup and received an A.M. as a show flower as lately as 1933.

'Damson', another Lanarth seedling, has as great a glow of true red in its cup as may be desirable to agree with a perianth of yellow shades. In strong light the glow of 'Damson's' cup is fascinating to play with. Both by reflection and transmission of light a fiery almost crimson effect can be produced by holding a flower in certain positions. This is equally remarkable whether on one side of the interior of the cup or on the base of a segment.

The general colour of the cup matches Rouge Saturne, Red Lead 58, Tone 1, of the French colour chart, and the glow on the interior can be as deep as 59, Tone 4, called Rouge Minium. The perianth is pale primrose becoming nearly white when mature, flushed at the base, without the streakiness found in 'Sunrise', with a clear lemon yellow, and it is a glorious flower for show and cutting.

'Trevisky' resembles its kinsman 'Damson' very closely in the colour of the cup, and has a flatter perianth of deep canary yellow of beautiful smooth texture, making it a singularly brilliant flower. A specimen grown with some protection was selected as the premier bloom of the 1924 Daffodil Show in London.

' Killigrew ' is one of the stronger growing members of this fraternity. The large sulphur perianth is paler at its tips and sets off the rich orange cup which holds its colour well in the open. ' Penquite ', ' Tregoose ' and ' Porthilly ' are good variations of the same colour scheme.

' Whiteley Gem ' is remarkable for its earliness, in which it beats its parent, which was ' Fortune ', a marvellous breeder that has furnished the Classified List with two pages of 2a offsprings, most of which bear its honoured, lucky name as part of theirs as a useful clue to their origin.

' Crœsus ' is an older production, and when in full colour worthy of the F.C.C. it won in 1912. Of those with a red rim to the cup ' Diolite ' is a good example. ' Helios ' raised by Mr. Engleheart received its award in 1912; it has been well grown in Holland, but having been overshadowed by the glamour of ' Fortune ' has not been used as much as it deserves as a garden plant in England. It has a well-proportioned, shapely yellow perianth and a pleasing vase-shaped cup, which under favourable conditions deepens in colour as it matures and can attain to a deep reddish orange when at its best. A vigorous habit and an 18-inch stem are recommendations that should not be overlooked.

Division 2b contains flowers with white or whitish perianth and self yellow, red-stained, or red cup. Of the first combination perhaps the best known is ' Great Warley ', an F.C.C. celebrity of 1904 raised by Mr. Engleheart. It is an immense flower with bright yellow widely expanded cup, contrasting well with the pure white perianth. Its peculiar form is well shown in a pencil sketch by H. G. Moon in *The Garden* for May 14th, 1904. The perianth is rather weak in substance and sets forward so much that it produces a lop-eared effect when looked at critically, but as a garden plant it is bold and distinct.

' Lady Margaret Boscawen ' gained a similar honour in 1898. It is smaller, deeper in the colour of the cup and has more substance in the perianth. ' Warden', ' Chancellor ' and ' Adjutant ' are more or less similar bicoloured forms, especially useful for cutting, lasting well because of their firm substance. In the open this virtue makes them top-heavy and liable to be beaten down in rough weather.

' Bodilly ' is one of the best later additions, and has a beautifully formed vase-shaped cup of clear yellow and a creamy almost white perianth of excellent substance, and is one of those flowers with a good back and a tall stem. ' Nissa ' has many good qualities: its poise, substance and form fit it for the show bench, and its bright yellow cup and tall habit for the garden. ' Warlock ' has a large flat flower, opening cream and changing to white, an open cup with a touch of red in its rim, and stands up bravely in bad weather.

' Bernardino ' is a well-known garden and market variety. It was raised by P. J. Worsley from ' Lulworth ', which was a self-sown seedling found in a Dorsetshire orchard and deriving from a poeticus variety what was then considered a surprisingly bright ring of colour on the cup. Bernardino has rather too much point to its segments and a rough-edged cup, but the soft apricot tint on its edge is charming.

' Eva ' has what haberdashers would call an outsize flower and is creating a stir, gaining awards and prizes wherever shown and a monetary value to match. Its flat perianth measures $4\frac{1}{2}$ inches across, and the yellow cup is edged with a bright orange, even band.

' Whitewell ', where it does well, has an individuality that makes it an outstanding variety. The creamy white perianth has a charming poise, and the inner segments standing forward from the wider outer ones provide lights and shadows and an alert expression seldom seen in so well-formed a flower. The coppery buff of the widely expanded cup is of an unusual colouring and very pleasing against the cream-coloured segments. I have admired it ever since the day I first saw it in Polman Mooy's garden in Haarlem, but it is a one-sided affection, and I fail to grow it well in my poor stony soil.

'Kennack' is a striking Cornish variety with a Nelsoni look about its rather narrow cup and stout substance. The apricot hue of the cup stands weather better than all others and deepens with age, and is set off by leaves of a delightful sea-green.

'Coverack Perfection', of 'Fortune' parentage, has a flat wide crown of most unusual form and colour, being edged with a wide band of pale orange with a pink salmon-coloured sheen in it that is wonderfully attractive.

'Galopin' is one of the famous 'Backhouse Reds' and a fine combination of ivory-white perianth with intensely orange cup. Most of these reds inherit their glory from 'Will Scarlett's' startlingly gaping, red mouth which always attracts attention in spite of crumpled perianth segments. 'Will Scarlett' was raised by Mr. Engleheart by pollen of N. poeticus poetarum on N. abscissus, and has always lived in the lime-light. Mr. Pope of King's Norton bought three bulbs for £100, Mr. Engleheart retaining the remaining three of the stock to breed from. This was the first instance of so large a sum being given for a daffodil, but proved so successful a speculation that others were encouraged to try their luck or judgment.

Bunches of its gaudy flowers have been selling in London shops and streets this season, and ordinary visitors to the garden always pick it out as the variety they would like to gather and carry away with them.

Perhaps when ' Folly ' is as well represented it will prove a superior attraction; to my mind it is the most splendid in Division 2*b* in colour, form and lasting quality. The purity of its crystalline white segments is enlivened by their unusual curves and reflexed position; they have a slight resemblance to one of the Turncap Lilies which is strengthened by the nodding poise of newly opened blossoms. The cup is of a beautifully symmetrical saucer-shape, regularly fluted and broadly but not deeply lobed, bright yellow shading upwards to a brilliant red-lead coloured band which covers the upper third of both inner and outer surfaces.

' Folly ' is tall, free flowering, late to open, lasts well into May and keeps its colour bravely in the open. Mr. P. D. Williams may raise a finer flower than ' Folly ' some day, but it is hard to believe he can improve on the peculiar charm of its brilliancy, gaiety and refinement.

Some there are who admire certain flowers of this division with irregularly lobed and fringed edges to their cups, as seen in ' John Evelyn ' and ' Scarlet Lancer '; others prefer a clean cut, symmetrical edge and think how much more pleasing these fringed flowers would be without this appearance of rags and malformation. It too frequently happens that the rough edge is associated with bleached patches suggesting arrested development or actual injury.

The fringes seen in the flowers of some Brassavolas and Dendrobiums, the Bog Bean and certain gourds are exquisitely beautiful owing to the fine regularity of their intricate designs, whereas a meaningless tangle of confused excrescences is a poor exchange for the beautiful outline to be found in the regularly lobed and toothed margins of the trumpets in some Ajax forms or the clean edge of a triandrus.

The puzzling little *N. Macleayi* is the Cinderella

of this group. Lindley described it in the *Botanical Register* under t. 762 in 1823. He saw it in the Horticultural Society's Garden, sent by Alexander Macleay, who is said to have received it from Smyrna. Curtis figured it in the *Botanical Magazine* t. 2588 for 1825, and Lindley in *Botanical Register* t. 987 for 1826. This last plate represents the flower as nearly 2 inches in diameter; in the *Botanical Magazine* it is only half as large. It is a dwarf plant with leaves too broad and pretentious for the size of the neat bicoloured flower, but it is distinct enough to look well at the foot of rocks.

As it occasionally produced two flowers to a scape it was thought to be ' a Tazetta become dwarf with an umbel reduced to two flowers '. It is more likely a hybrid between a poeticus and perhaps the bicolor abscissus. It seems to be Parkinson's Small early white Daffodil with a long cup of p. 73 and Fig. 7 of p. 71. There is a good figure showing the habit in *The Garden*, February 17th, 1906, and Burbidge's Pl. 17 is excellent.

N. Sabinii is described and figured in *Bot. Reg.* t. 762. It differs from Macleayi in larger flowers, with cream-coloured segments and a pleated corona much waved at the edge. Lindley saw it among a collection formed by Sabine and given by him to the Horticultural Society's Garden. Sabine received it in 1818 from the Oxford Botanical Garden. It has apparently been lost, though it must have been a better looking plant than Macleayi.

A race of somewhat similar forms was raised in gardens and named *Nelsonii* after the Rev. John G. Nelson, who raised Daffodils and other plants at Aldborough Rectory, Norfolk, and died in 1882. Several varieties bearing specific names formed on too botanical a practice for such purely horticultural plants were popular at the end of the last century.

The best was Nelsonii aurantius, which in some
seasons showed a good deal of orange coloration at
the mouth of the corona.   They all had a nodding
pose, nearly white perianths with more or less recurving
edges to the segments rendering them rather starry in
effect, and their chief merit lay in a late-flowering
habit and a good constitution.   The variety major is
figured in *The Garden* for September 24th, 1898.   My
favourite form is var. pulchellus, which is dwarf with
wide overlapping segments and a neatly formed yellow
cup of almost triandrus outline.

N. *Bernardii* of De Candolle, the natural hybrid
found in the Pyrenees wherever N. poeticus and
abscissus grow together, is very variable, as might
be expected with two such parents.   Short- or long-
cupped forms have been found.   Burbidge contributed a note on wild specimens found near Luchon
to the *Gardeners' Chronicle*, July 16th, 1881.   I have
found a few specimens in that same neighbourhood.
Like many of the poeticus forms from considerable altitudes, they are not very happy in English
gardens.

The Incomparabilis section has more than any other
produced double-flowered forms of great beauty.
Besides the old-fashioned cottage garden favourites
named after various combinations of victuals, nurserymen's lists contain many recently raised varieties,
which should be more frequently grown in gardens.
Those that are not too heavily packed with extra
segments make a brave show in fair-sized groups
among shrubs or herbaceous plants.   All kinds are
useful for cutting, lasting long and providing very
decorative effects of mingled colours when several
varieties are mixed together in a wide-mouthed vase.

'Apricot Phœnix' has soft sulphur as the prevailing hue, shading to a buffish apricot colouring at
the base of the segments and deepening towards the

centre wonderfully like that of some tea roses. 'Primrose Phœnix' is a good self yellow of a deep primrose colour, very fully double with six whorls of well-formed perianth segments. 'Plenipo' has a rounder flower rather tightly packed with alternations of light and dark yellow. 'Silver Rose' has a creamy white perianth of good form succeeded by a more or less cut-up corona just the colour of Cornish cream, and the centre is filled up with less regularly formed whorls of both colours. It has a good substance and lasting qualities, but is so heavy that it is better for cutting than for making a show in the border.

'Twink' is also good for cutting with full heads of white and orange. 'Irene Copeland' fills the same rôle, as it is too large in the head to be graceful. It has queer little, yellow, strap-shaped coronal pieces placed at regular intervals in its mass of white perianth segments, and is very telling when mixed with others in a vase.

'Inglescombe' is much like 'Primrose Phœnix' and 'Golden Rose', but has rather longer and better shaped perianth segments.

'Milk and Honey' lives up to its name in its colour scheme, and with many other good doubles was raised by Mr. Copeland, whose 'Mary Copeland' is perhaps the best of the Incomparabilis doubles. Its regular form and glistening whiteness contrasting with the intense orange scarlet coronal pieces make it too good for a mixed bunch, and it should share a vase of good, old glass with a few leaves picked from a less distinguished variety. 'The Pearl' should also show the full length of its stem to set off the delicate primrose-coloured, well-formed flowers.

Mr. Engleheart's 'Argent' has grown in our gardens for a quarter of a century and is still one of the best; its long and narrow perianth segments are nearly white and contrast beautifully with the bright yellow of the coronal pieces scattered among them. It has a particularly graceful outline and a long stiff stem, so that a bunch of cut blossoms should be arranged loosely. They are charming placed among twigs of Sweet Gale when bearing its small brown catkins.

X

BARRII AND BURBIDGEI

DIVISION III. is distinguished from Division II. (Incomparabilis) by its shorter corona, which must be less than a third of the length of the perianth segments.

Both Barrii and Burbidgei varieties are of garden origin, the result of crossing forms of poeticus and incomparabilis. The two races were separated at one time according to the degree of resemblance they bore to one or other parent. Those most resembling incomparabilis were reckoned to belong to the Barrii section, those with white, smaller flowers and flatter cups to Burbidgei. However, so many border-line plants appeared that both were classed as Division III., called Barrii, with section (a) for those with yellow perianths and section (b) for those with white or whitish perianths.

The original forms of Barrii were raised by W. Backhouse of Wolsingham, Durham, the raiser of the well-known Trumpet varieties ' Emperor ' and ' Empress '.

N. Barrii conspicuus received a F.C.C. in 1886 and is still the best known and most useful variety. It is never sick or sorry in borders or grass, spreads rapidly, but will flower even after it has grown into a crowded clump. The perianth is a bright yellow at first and grows paler, especially in the centre of each segment, with age, when the softened colouring goes better with the very brilliant red rim of the cup.

It sported in a curious way and produced a variety with pure white perianth which was named ' Branston ' and received an A.M. in 1903. Unfortunately this form never became fixed and frequently reverted to the type, or too often to an ugly piebald condition with both white and yellow segments. 'Lady Godiva', also called 'Barbara Holmes', had a similar origin. 'Crown Prince' and 'Crown Princess', two others raised by W. Backhouse with white or nearly white perianths, have been surpassed by modern forms and are now found among the varieties in small type of the 1933 *Classified List*.

There are very few good varieties of 3*a* that have no red or orange in the corona. 'St. Egwin' is the best to date. A tall flower over 4 inches in diameter, of soft yellow throughout the wide perianth and short cup, it stands out conspicuously in garden and show bench and is refined and beautifully proportioned in spite of its size. But 'St. Egwin' is still valued at a pound an inch. Pl. 119 in Mr. Calvert's *Daffodil Growing* shows its size and form.

Those with red-rimmed cups are more numerous. After conspicuus, 'Bath's Flame' is one of the most popular; being rather gaudy and very early it is a most successful market flower.

'Brilliancy' gives another early flare of colour. 'Seraglio' has a paler perianth that goes well with its bright yellow, orange-rimmed cup, and as it is said to be a rapid increaser we may hope its price will decrease in inverse ratio to the number of its offsets. 'Midas', like the first of its name, no longer touches gold. It has a beautifully rounded large flower with a soft yellow perianth and a cup edged with a narrow red line.

The most dainty and refined of this group is 'Dinkie', raised by Mr. Herbert Chapman. He has told us that it was 'by crossing "Princess Mary" with "Crimson Braid"' and that 'Dinkie' was a grandchild of 'Will Scarlett', whose deplorable perianth was corrected into a perfection of roundness by

a union with the small, round-flowered poeticus once
known as verus of Linnæus, which Mr. Pugsley
recognises as a Greek form and names hellenicus.

' Dinkie ' has inherited its forbears' good points,
and has apparently dropped their vices. Grandma
hellenicus reflexes badly and so does Mme. Crimson
Braid, but ' Dinkie ' holds herself in a charming
butterfly-wing pose, has a complexion of wax-like
substance and a most unusual shade of yellow with
a dash of green in it, and a rimmed cup that any poeticus
could be proud of. The red line is as fine as, but far
more beautiful than, a plucked eyebrow. The portrait
in *Gardening Illustrated*, April 22nd, 1933, does not
suggest the delicate colouring of the cup.

' Brightling ' is very showy, with a round primrose
yellow perianth and a yellow cup edged with deep
orange, curiously frilled and lobed, giving the appearance of three ranks of coronal pieces.

Many fine varieties are available now with cups
of solid orange or shading to margins of glowing red.
' Nanny Nunn ' and ' Marquis ', raised by Mrs. R. O.
Backhouse, are vigorous growers. The former is cheap
enough for its red-orange cup to glow in every garden,
the ' Marquis ' red enough to be worth paper money.

' Treskerby ', ' Garlidna ', ' Alight ' and ' Tredore ',
raised in Cornwall, possess the substance and finish
of perianth for which the Lanarth strain is noted and
fiery red cups. The first two can be bought for
shillings, the others for pounds. ' Treskerby ' is a
fine garden plant and gave a good account of its increase, freedom of flowering, size and quality of
blooms in the Wisley Trials. ' Market Merry ', from
The Brodie, we are told may beat the rest by its
earliness and rich colouring, but the stock is still small,
so its price is not.

Forms with pale perianths came to the fore when
Mr. Engleheart allowed ' Albatross ' and ' Seagull '

to fly over his garden wall in the nineties. Though we now look more critically at their long and twisting wings when, for show purposes, we regard them as perianths, they are still excellent garden varieties. They are free-flowering, good increasers and among the best for planting in drifts to give a mass of pleasant, cool colour among clumps of herbaceous plants which will flower later. Both came from the same seedpod of N. poeticus pollinated by ' Empress '. The orange ring in ' Albatross ' is very bright in the young flower, and lasts well if the blossom is gathered before the sun can fade it. ' Seagull' has only a suggestion of orange, which disappears quickly, leaving a bright yellow cup. Both were figured in *The Garden*, April 22nd, 1893.

In ' St. Anthony ' Mrs. Backhouse produced a taller and whiter flower with flatter perianth and a curiously small cup with a delightful tint of salmon pink round its edge. From a distance it stands out as an unusually white flower, as its back is as white as its face, in which it resembles some Leedsii varieties— ' White Lady ', for instance. ' Lidcot ' from the same raiser also has a delicately coloured cup of citron yellow with a red ring.

' Circlet ', from Mr. Engleheart, is such a neat, tenderly coloured flower that, though it is dwarf and small, it is worth preserving as a garden plant and to pick for a small vase. A coloured portrait appeared in *The Garden* for August 13th, 1910, which shows its rounded perianth and neat, red-edged cup very truthfully. ' Queen of Hearts ' has a larger, similarly well-formed flower with a deep orange cup and is worth remembering.

' Sunrise ' is too well known as a popular market flower to need lengthy description. It is one of the earliest to provide the brilliantly coloured cup the public welcomes as a change in the programme from yellow trumpets. Its white perianth is streaked at the base with rays of bright yellow, spreading out from the yellow, red-edged cup; hence its attractive name. For cutting it is excellent, but must not be allowed to see the real sun. Half-opened buds develop their full beauty indoors. It is unsuitable for garden decoration, burning quickly and possessing limp, yellowish green leaves, which always look unhealthy, and die off early in May in an unpleasant brown and yellow collapse.

Flowers of smaller build with slightly reflexed perianths are useful for cutting for small vases for a dinner table or where seen at close range. ' Cossack ', opening yellow, then turning white, and ' Bullfinch ', white from the first, look well mixed with ' Glitter ' and ' Mars ', which are 3*a*'s, as they retain the yellow in the perianth.

Many Barrii varieties have appeared which are almost Poets, having pure white perianths and crimson ringed cups. Of such is Mr. Herbert Chapman's celebrated ' Crimson Braid ', a perfectly formed show flower, if it can wear a back board or strait-jacket up to the time when the warning bell clears it off along with the exhibitors before the judges commence their work. In a two-days' show it sometimes reflexes so much that it can be unrecognisable by the end of the second afternoon.

' Lady Moore ', raised by Polman Mooy, ' Miss Willmott ' and ' King George V ' by van Tubergen, are other fine showy examples of Barriis closely resembling poeticus varieties. ' Mithian ' is so much on the border-line as to be classed sometimes in 9, sometimes, as in Mr. Richardson's list, as 3*b*. ' Turin ' has a red edge and a green centre, almost those of a poeticus.

The next step in development produced the pure white perianth and deep red cups that are the glory of 3*b*.

The most fiery red cup has provoked the name
' Hades '. It has been described as ' cherry red
throughout ', and that cannot be bettered.   Mrs. Backhouse set it alight, and it obtained Awards of Merit
at R.H.S. and Birmingham.   Another of her seedlings,
' Red Planet ', is also surprisingly red.

From Lanarth came ' Carminowe ' with a wonderfully glistening white perianth and flat crimson eye,
perfect in their contrast.   This won the Medal for the
best bloom at the London Daffodil Show of 1929, and I
believe can do it again.   ' Roxana ', ' Kilter ' and
' Picador ', also from Lanarth, have more of orange
in their red, and the last is a smaller but perfectly
formed flower.   These are among the *élite* at present.
' Red Beacon ', an older Cornish seedling, is plentiful
and good enough to represent the red-cupped race in
any garden.

' Firetail ', raised by the late E. M. Crosfield, is
deservedly popular as a market flower; its flat, creamy
to pure white perianth, glowing cup and slightly
pendulous poise give a freedom from that stiffness
associated with certain flowers of show form.   It is
not easy to grow everywhere, apparently objecting to
heavy, moist soil, but it can be placated by planting
the bulbs in a liberal layer of sand, and it is well worth
that trouble.   ' Dick Turpin ' (frontispiece), another
Crosfield seedling, combines an ivory-white perianth
with a perfectly flat, deep red corona slightly paler in
the centre.   In ' Sacrifice ' (facing page 106) the corona
is more uniform in colour and a brilliant orange-red.

Before long there may be a division provided to
contain varieties with a flush of pink in the perianth.
' John Peel ', raised by the late Dr. Lower, ' Belle
Chinoise ' from Mr. Alec Wilson, and a newcomer
' Bosloe ' already exist with colouring approaching
that of a prawn cooked and peeled.

XI

LEEDSII

THE R.H.S. Division IV. (Leedsii) has perianth white, corona white, cream or pale citron, sometimes tinged with pink or apricot.

This race was first produced by Edward Leeds, who died in 1877, and is named in his honour. It is the result of crossing white forms of Ajax with poeticus, and it follows naturally that some of the progeny will be on the border-line close to bicoloured forms of Incomparabilis, and others with the short cup of poeticus more evident will resemble Barrii forms. It is therefore chiefly by the pallor of any colouring present that such flowers can be recognised as belonging to Leedsii.

In 1915 the Leedsii division was subdivided according to the comparative length of the corona and perianth. Section *a*, Giant Leedsii, requires the corona to be not less than one-third, but less than equal to, the length of the perianth segments. Section *b* must have the cup, as in Barrii varieties, less than one-third the length of the segments.

It is interesting but rather sad to look back at the Leedsii forms that gained awards fifty years ago and onwards to the close of the last century. First-Class Certificates were awarded to ' Queen of England ' and ' Minnie Hume ' in 1884, ' Duchess of Westminster ' in 1886, ' White Lady ' in 1898 and ' Maggie May ' in 1899, some of which would be burnt on the evidence of their perianths if they appeared among modern seedlings.

' White Lady ' still receives respectful treatment,

having a fine, wide, white perianth with a good back
to it. She can provide as good a drift of white as any
poeticus, but of the whited sepulchre nature, for inside
there is a cup so ragged that it would disgrace any
recent seedling. It has been described as ' daintily
crimped ', though to others it suggests the remains
of a slug's hearty meal. For distant effect plant
' White Lady ' freely, but do not look into her face.

' Queen of the North ', ' Evangeline ' and ' Fairy
Queen ', if already in the garden, are worth leaving
in the beds for cutting. They are of a useful size and
beautifully white.

For lovely flowers to show, or to gather for your
desk or dinner table, which means for looking at
closely, there are some exquisite small-cupped Leedsii
varieties. ' Silver Salver ', the purest white of any,
has a flat cup so beautifully crystalline that The
Brodie's apt name for it could not be bettered. A
touch of emerald green in the throat prevents the effect
of a dead whiteness and gives it a lively expression.

' Samaria ' is very similar in beauty of form and
texture. The cup is less expanded and of a softer,
creamy white. A lovely flower until placed beside
' Silver Salver ', when we notice that the green eye is
lacking.

' Cushendall ', raised by Mr. Guy Wilson, has the
best green eye of any variety. He is right in calling it
moss green, for it is a rich and dark green with no
cold blue tone about it. The corona has a slight shade
of yellow at its edge that gives a wonderful finish to
this lovely but expensive flower.

' Addio ' flowers so late that it has only poeticus
recurvus as a rival.

The Giant Leedsii seedlings classed as 4a owe their
size and beauty to the larger and more robust Ajax
forms that were available for crossing.

' White Queen ', from Mr. Engleheart, seemed in

1898 to deserve its F.C.C. as the best white flower of
its day. Mr. Kingsmill grew it well at Harrow Weald,
and the bunch of its white flowers he brought into
this house opened our eyes to the deficiencies of the
Leedsii forms then in the garden. It is too dwarf
to be really effective in most gardens, and has
gone into small type in the list, surpassed by 'Lord
Kitchener', raised by Mrs. Backhouse. This tall, well-
built flower becomes almost white throughout when
mature, and is still one of the best for garden and
cutting, and better than the somewhat similar 'Sirdar'
and Pearson's 'Hon. Mrs. J. L. Francklin', neither
of which should be despised by those who are not
prepared to pay big prices.

'Niveth' is classed as a Leedsii, though it is a
Leedsii and triandrus hybrid. It possesses unusual
vigour for a variety showing so much of the grace
and purity of triandrus.

For perfection of form, substance and whiteness
at a florin a bulb, 'White Nile' is at present hard to
beat, and being a free increaser will pay a good dividend.
Even the immense 'Tenedos', which has been called
a white 'Great Warley', is within the spending power
of a modest purse. The spread of its long perianth
segments has a fascinating likeness to the wings of
a bird, or, since they number six, it would be more
correct to say of a seraph.

'Syra', another extra large flower, 'Marmora',
smaller, and 'Mitylene' with its widely expanded
crown, are all magnificently white and inexpensive.
'Gyrfalcon' is rather heavy and rough compared with
these, but has a marvellous substance and sturdiness
which carry it safely through the weather its early-
flowering habit forces it to face.

Of those with a dash of cream or lemon in the corona
the most perfect for form, poise, purity of white
in the perianth and a delicate tint of primrose in the

8

young crown, ' Niphetos ' must surely stand first for
many a day. Its portrait given opposite was drawn
at its birthplace Lanarth, but needs a profile view as
well to show the symmetry and beauty of proportion
between perianth and corona.

' Grayling ', ' Selene ', ' Cicely ' and ' Harebell '
run down the scale of prices, and all are beautiful,
starting life with some lemon yellow in the corona
which almost disappears as they age. ' Cicely ' and
' Harebell ' are among the first white flowers to
open.

' Ettrick ' retains some of its primrose colouring
throughout its flowering period. ' Silver Plane ' was
raised in New Zealand by the late Arthur E. Lowe, and
is unlike anything else in the large, flat cup of a bright
yellow which contrasts admirably with the broad white
perianth.

Among those with decidedly lemon-yellow coronas
' May Molony ' stands first; not very large but of
fine finish and texture, it is lovely grown in a pot
without being forced at all and one of the latest to
flower when grown in the open.

Another strain shows a more or less distinct rim of
colour to the corona inherited from the poeticus
parent. ' Tunis ' is a bold early flower whose frilled
crown deepens with age until the mouth is decidedly
buff. ' Brunswick ' is newer and even better for
colour, developing a clear yellow rim when fully out.
' Hymettus ' has a shorter cup with a lemon-yellow
edge. ' Nelly ' achieves a tint of orange. ' Fairy
Circle ', a small flower (4b) with a flat cup, achieves
a decidedly pink rim. ' New Moon ', another 4b, has a
wonderfully large flat white cup edged with a perfectly
even band of an astonishingly brilliant orange-red;
it flowers late and is one of the most distinct in form
and colour.

' Mystic ' is another of Mr. Guy Wilson's successes

in seedlings of original design. It is a tall late variety
with much poeticus influence in it—not really white,
having a charming mingling of a creamy tint with an
almost imaginary shading of greenness in it, something like that of the Japanese Cherry Yukon, which
looks as though seen through water. The cup is
large and flat, white with a green centre and a beautifully regular rim of coral red so soft in colour that it
has none of the hard look of a narrowly rimmed
poeticus.

So-called ' pink-cupped ' varieties have been much
admired or roundly abused according to the fancy of
the critic. The fact is that no really rose-pink form
has yet been seen by the general public—though it
may not be long before a separate class has to be made
for those now in the nursery.

The late Mrs. R. O. Backhouse raised the first. It
bears her honoured name and was shown in 1923.
Though it had more pink in it than any previously
known, there is also so much pale orange in the lower
portion of the corona that the general effect is nearer
to a pale apricot shade, with a salmon-pink rim when
at its best. It is a wonderful flower, colours well
out of doors and stands out conspicuously enough
to be noticed by all, though most people are reluctant
to accept it as a pink Daffodil.

' Suda ', raised by The Brodie of Brodie, gained an
A.M. in 1927. It was bred from ' Lord Kitchener '
and the White Trumpet ' Nevis '. In a congenial,
equable climate the cup can take on what has been
called ' a lovely pale clear amber rose colour ' as the
flowers mature in the open, but blossoms gathered
early and opened under cover remain white to the
end.

One day no doubt Leedsii seedlings will bear cups
suffused with a real salmon pink such as has appeared
in the rims of some. Mr. Cranfield's seedling ' Miss

E. M. Bowling ' was the best so far and received an
A.M. in 1918, but unfortunately was entirely destroyed
by eelworm.

At present the amount of pink suffusion is like the
jam in a doughnut, enough to stain but too little to
satisfy.

XII

TRIANDRUS

LINNÆUS APPLIED this somewhat ridiculous name to the plant Clusius called N. juncifolius flore albo reflexo and described in the *Auctarium* to the Second Appendix to his *Historia*, a portion of the great work troublesome to find, being generally bound in with the *Curiae Posteriores* of 1611 and without pagination. The excellent woodcut block illustrating it was used again in Johnson's Gerard.

The three longer stamens are shown protruding beyond the corona, and it seems that Clusius over-looked the three shorter ones in the tube, as his description limits them to three. This apparently led Linnæus to use the name triandrus when he described it in the Second Edition of *Species Plantarum*. He stated, however, ' stamina tria (mihi ut Clusii) raro sex quae tamen in quibusdam vidi individuis '.

Clusius received the bulbs from Nicholas le Quelt, who collected rare plants in the Pyrenees and Spain.

N. triandrus is now recognised as the name for an assemblage of wild forms varying by minute differences from pure white to deep yellow, from one to six flowers in a scape, and from a short, rounded corona, as in var. concolor, to long, vase-shaped, and sometimes lobed, bells nearly as long as the segments.

N. triandrus is widely distributed in Portugal and Western Spain, but is only represented in France by the largest and whitest form, which has a very limited range on Drenec, one of the Islands of the Glenans, about thirty miles off the coast of Finisterre.

The typical form must be that of Linnæus with flowers altogether white, and the corona half as long as the perianth, according to the expanded description he gave in the Third Edition of *Species Plantarum*. He also cites the plant Clusius described as having flowers of snowy whiteness. This is best represented in the variety known as N. triandrus albus, although it varies in colour from white to pale sulphur and end-lessly as to the shape and length of the corona.

Mr. Barr has kindly lent me a number of specimens collected in Portugal by Mr. Tait in the eighties of last century. The coronas in some are as large as those of the French plant, in others short and round, or straight-sided and narrow. Four types of variation are shown in an excellent sketch made by Mr. Engle-heart and reproduced in *The Garden* for March 12th, 1887.

A plant with such a wide range of variation provides tempting opportunities for botanists who are addicted to the coining of names. Accordingly Salisbury in 1812 placed the French variety in his genus Queltia with incomparabilis, on the evidence of Redouté's Pl. 177 and De Candolle's description in *Les Liliacées*, vol. iii., 1807, and changed the specific name to capax. He also made a new genus Ganymedes for forms with shorter coronas.

Haworth in his *Monograph* (1831) adopted Salis-bury's Ganymedes for forms with coronas three to four times shorter than the perianth segments. He created a genus Illus (named after one of the brothers of Ganymedes) for forms with coronas about half as long as the segments, and chose another brother's name, Assaracus, for Redouté's two figures of the French variety, calling t. 177 A. capax and t. 410 A. reflexus, following Schultes in Roemer's *Systema Vegetabilium*.

There is a good coloured plate in vol. xxxiv. of *The*

Garden, by Moon, showing varieties of the pure white form, also represented in Parkinson's Fig. 2, p. 93, of the *Paradisus*, called N. juncifolius flore albo reflexo, and C. de Pas's Fig. 2 on Pl. 23 Ver of the *Hortus Floridus*.

Slightly sulphur-tinted forms, such as Curtis's t. 48 of the *Botanical Magazine*, according to Salisbury should be G. cernuus. He tells us that it was introduced by Edward Gray, M.D., in 1777 from Oporto, and ripened seed in the borders at Chapel Allerton, but flourished better in a pot under a frame. Curtis says it is ' pale yellow but colour is not in the least to be depended on for it is found to vary in this as in all the other species '. Therefore the name cernuus does not seem worth retaining, seeing that N. pallidulus of Graells is of a rather more decided shade of primrose. This is figured in the *Bot. Mag.*, t. 6473, described as pale sulphur, but owing to some fault of the colourist or the pigment it is represented as incredibly and unpleasantly green.

Var. concolor is generally small and slender, with a very short corona and of a decided yellow throughout. It is the G. concolor of Haworth, ' the self-coloured ' in his *Monograph*, and Parkinson's Yellow turning Junquilia, described as ' wholly of a gold yellow colour, both the cuppe and the leaves that turn up again '. The plant grown by Dr. Giuseppi as aurantiacus pallidulus seems to be a deeply coloured form of this.

Var. pulchellus is one of the best and most interesting. It is remarkable as one of the few forms of Narcissus with a corona paler than the perianth. It is Parkinson's Yellow turning Junquilia with a white cup, and Salisbury's and Haworth's G. pulchellus, ' the pretty white-cupped ', a well-deserved name. The *Bot. Mag.*, t. 1262, is cited in Baker's *Amaryllideae* for this variety, though Gawler called

it var. luteus, and stated it to be very variable
in colour. The corona is of the right size and shape
for pulchellus, but hardly white enough. Sweet's
t. 99 in the Second Series of the *British Flower Garden*
is excellent and shows a good form with a greater
contrast of colour between perianth and corona.

Salisbury knew the plant well and had reason to
remember it. He tells us that it was for many years
confined to gardens about Halifax in Yorkshire, where
he helped to propagate it when at school in that neighbourhood, and was flogged in the Whitsuntide holidays
of 1769 for running out of bounds to know the name
of it at North Bierly. He goes on to say that London
nurserymen had pretty well cleared the North of it,
' and if they will only make it plentiful in the South
I shall rejoice '.

He continues: ' The surest method of doing this,
is to plant the bulbs in a border of pure loam, rather
moist than dry; about once in four or five years as soon
as the leaves are decayed, they should be taken up
and transplanted, but not often, for I have found
this, and many other bulbous-rooted plants, succeed
better by not being too frequently removed, their
leaves sheltering one another in snow or storms, so
that if the ends are cut, the lower part remains green.'
How clearly the character of a good gardener is
revealed in these instances of his youthful zeal and
ripe experience !

He thought the *Botanical Magazine* plate was taken
from a weak specimen, as there were generally three to
five and sometimes seven flowers on a stem.

This is a variety that should be made much of, as
it is more vigorous and more easily grown than others.
It has been raised from seed occasionally, and is
worthy of every care that could help to further Salisbury's pious wish.

Although Burbidge states that his Pl. 15 represents

pulchellus, it contains two forms, one pale sulphur like pallidulus, the other all yellow like concolor. Burbidge thought Parkinson called this group Turning Junquilia because the leaves and scapes were twisted, but by turning leaves Parkinson meant the perianth. The *Bot. Mag.* t. 48 shows curved leaves and a remarkable scape with a spiral arrangement of ridges unlike anything I have noticed in living specimens. This drawing may have suggested the idea to Burbidge.

Every variety of triandrus is beautiful in shape and graceful in habit. The narrow leaves and slender scapes fit them for the choicest place among small plants in a rock garden. The flowers are pendent with the perianth turned upwards from the corona to lie against the tube and ovary, every segment being slightly twisted so that they resemble the petals of a cyclamen. In those varieties in which the three long stamens and the pistil protrude beyond the hanging corona they have an outline rather like that of a Fuchsia. They are most elegant and charming when bearing one or two flowers on a scape, but clusters of four or five are not to be despised and encourage their owner to feel the plants are strong and happy.

Coming from South-Western Europe they require some protection, especially from drying winds in early Spring. They ask for a gritty, well-drained soil round the bulbs and some good loam lower down for the roots to reach in the growing season.

Many extremely lovely hybrids have been raised by crossing juncifolius and triandrus, and some of them possess a vigour lacking in their parents and also the virtue of increasing freely by offsets. Both of the parent species generally become exhausted if allowed to bear seed, which they frequently set without artificial pollination, whereas the hybrids seem chary of doing so.

Where N. triandrus and N. Bulbocodium meet in

Portugal hybrid forms occur that are not so attractive
as their parents; but a pleasing race called N. trimon
resulted from crossing N. Bulbocodium monophyllus
with a triandrus. An illustration from a water-colour
drawing was published in *The Garden*, December
29th, 1894, and another from a photograph on
March 10th, 1900. As so little has been seen of them
they probably proved difficult to cultivate.

N. triandrus var. calathinus. The large form from
the Iles des Glenans has given both pleasure and
trouble in plenty to botanists and gardeners.

The former have questioned its status as a species
or variety and have disputed over its name. Many
have used calathinus as a specific name, but, as it can
be shown, incorrectly.

Linnæus evidently did not know the plant, which
was discovered by Bonnemaison of Quimper early
in the nineteenth century. De Candolle in *Les
Liliacées*, vol. iii., 1807, wrote that he received the
specimen from which Pl. 177 was drawn from Bonnemaison. It is fairly clear that Redouté drew it from
a dried or recently pressed flower, which would account
for its curious yellow colouring, similar to that of
Burbidge's Pl. 14, which was drawn from herbarium
specimens. Again, the perspective of the perianth
is wrong: the nearest central segment is laid back flat,
and the one behind the corona is flattened out forwards
in a position that Redouté could not have seen in a
living specimen with a normally reflexed perianth.
He afterwards made amends in the correctly drawn and
coloured Pl. 410 of vol. vii. of the same work.

De Candolle applied Linnæus's name calathinus
to this new plant, misled by Linnæus's description
of the corona as equal to the petals in length. Sims,
however, in 1806 pointed out that Linnæus's calathinus
was a form of N. odorus, as may be seen under t. 934
of the *Botanical Magazine*.

Herbert in *Amaryllidaceae*, p. 313, 1837, went into the matter fully and concluded that Linnæus never had a specimen, ' but named it, in MS. on the margin of the first Edition of *Species Plantarum*, and published it in the second with a reference to Clusius, No. 1. juncif. 9. and Rudbeck *Campi Elysii*, 2. p. 60. Fig. 5. Rudbeck's figure is a very unfaithful copy of Clusius's with a reference to it, therefore the original plant of Clusius is the thing meant, and that corresponds very closely with N. calathinus *Bot. Mag.* Rudbeck exaggerated the size of the cup in his engraving, on the faith of which Linnæus described it as having the cup and limb nearly equal, but no such specimen has ever been forthcoming, and as Linnæus had no specimen, but meant to describe the plant of Clusius, we must look to Clusius alone, rejecting the garbled figure of Rudbeck.'

Reference to Clusius shows that the plant he saw flowering at Leyden was yellow, the perianth not reflexed and the cup only half the length of the perianth and decidedly a variety of N. odorus. Bauhin's *Pinax* cites Clusius's plant as N. angustifolius flavus magno calice.[1] Therefore the name calathinus belongs to a yellow flower which, as Linnæus states, is like Tazetta but with larger and more pointed petals, and this agrees best with N. odorus. Further evidence that De Candolle's specimen had been pressed and dried before he described it is found in his description ' la fleur est jaune ', and of the perianth ' six lanières très-étalées '. Again, in this drawing the leaves are too wide and flat and the bulb is wrong in shape and size, and both seem to have been added without a living specimen as a model.

The second figure in vol. vii., t. 410, is much better as to leaf and bulb and has white flowers with reflexed perianths. It seems to have been drawn from a

---

[1] Not ' caulo ', as in *Les Liliacées*.

specimen seen in M. Vilmorin's garden in Paris. The text of this volume was written by Alire Raffeneau-Delile, who, like De Candolle, describes the corona as being the length of the perianth. Both men must have deceived themselves on this point, for both of the figures, and the dissection accompanying the second, show the segments fully a tenth of an inch longer than the corona.

Then Salisbury's Queltia capax enters the lists, published in 1812 in *Trans. Hort. Soc. London*, to replace De Candolle's N. calathinus, but without a description. Salisbury says it grew in the Glenans Isles and that it flowered at Walworth twenty years previously, a single root having been imported from Holland. This seems too early and is rather slight evidence that the real plant is intended. Haworth uses capax in his genus Assaracus for Redouté's first plate, and describes it as yellow and cites N. capax of Schultes's *Systema Veg.*, 7, 950. For the second plate, 410, he chose reflexus, the name Schultes used in *Syst. Veg.*, 7, 952 also for the white plant.

If the Glenans plant is regarded as a species of Narcissus, it is not entitled to be called either N. calathinus or N. capax; and as it differs from N. triandrus merely in the greater size of its flowers and its restricted geographical range, it may properly be regarded as a variety of that variable species and the name N. triandrus var. calathinus should be used for it.

Gardeners find this desirable plant liable to die out unless frequently renewed from seed. Except in very sheltered gardens it should be grown in pans with good drainage, so that it may be stood in a saucer to provide a good supply of water from below in the growing season, and be dried off when it should remain dormant. In a few places it will sow itself freely in the open, but they are all too few. It has been noticed that though it can stand severe frost if dry it resents damp and cold together. It is well worth the protection of a frame or cool house for the sake of its exquisitely formed white flowers, as also for the sake of its pollen, which has proved wonderfully potent when used upon very different seed parents. Its most marked influence is the whiteness it conveys to nearly all seedlings. Smoothness of texture and a pendent poise generally appear also.

Triandrus Hybrids are now so numerous that the R.H.S. Classification includes a Division V. for them, and this is subdivided into:

a. With long corona not less than a third of the perianth segments.

b. With short corona less than a third of the length of the perianth segments.

Section *a* contains the beautiful sulphur-coloured N. Johnstonii found in Portugal and described by J. G. Baker in *Gard. Chron.*, xxv., p. 590, in 1886. It was discovered in 1885 by Messrs. A. W. Tait and E. Johnston near Oporto, and it also grows in Galicia in Spain. Where found it was in great abundance, but has been heavily and greedily collected, too often to languish and die in English gardens.

Its abundance and slight range of variation have been taken as evidence against a hybrid origin; however, similar forms have been raised frequently in gardens by crossing N. triandrus with a yellow Ajax. The earliest is figured in *The Garden*, August 16th, 1890, p. 153, and was raised by Mr. Engleheart by fertilising 'Emperor' with pollen of triandrus. In the insertion of the anthers the hybrid resembles N. Johnstonii, in which they are in two ranks. Two larger flowers of the same parentage are shown in the plate by Moon in *The Garden*, July 18th, 1896. Others are shown in beautiful engravings in *Flora and Sylva*, vol. iii. One named 'Count Visconti' resembles Johnstonii closely, but is of garden origin and of larger size. 'Earl Grey', another triandrus and 'Emperor' cross, is a bicolor. I have some seedling forms raised by Mr. Herbert Chapman that closely resemble the wild plant.

N. Johnstonii was largely collected by Mr. Peter Barr and has been widely distributed as 'Queen of Spain', but does not flourish satisfactorily in many gardens. Some succeed with it if planted in grass; here I find it is better planted on a steep, sunny slope in the rock garden, and it has grown well in such a position at Great Warley.

Its drooping, sulphur flowers are hard to beat when it does well. The perianth is slightly reflexed and the long corona is beautifully smooth and mostly straight-edged. Forms with a spreading brim were at one time called 'King of Spain', but the name has been dropped as it seems to be little more than a seasonal variation which frequently reverts to the usual straight-cupped form.

A distinct form is grown in the Hocker Edge Gardens that is more uniform and may be a clone. It also possesses the virtue of increasing more freely than the older form.

The figure t. 7012 of the *Botanical Magazine* is not good; the flowers are too stiff in position and the colouring not sufficiently clean.

Among early raised 5a seedlings were 'J. T. Bennett-Poë' and 'The Rev. Charles Digby', pale primrose forms which received awards but are seldom seen now. 'Viscountess Falmouth', paler and more like a 2b in form, is now superseded by other kinds. One of the best is 'Harvest Moon', a lemon-coloured self, with a wide cup of fine texture; and a glorious thing when grown in a pot and protected under glass but not forced.

Of large, white triandrus seedlings 'Viscountess

Northcliffe', raised by Mrs. Backhouse, is one of the most remarkable. The large flowers are so solidly white, the trumpet so straight and cleanly cut. If it has a fault it is found in the rather short stem. 'Snowdon', one of Mr. H. Prins' seedlings, is almost an Ajax in form and has a long, narrow, cream-coloured corona fluted at the brim and is a distinct flower.

The 5*b* Section contains flowers even more graceful in form, and some are so purely white that they resemble a Eucharis.

'Venetia', raised by Mr. H. Backhouse, is as perfect as any when good, but is not happy everywhere, too often producing thin yellowish foliage and small flowers. Where it grows strongly it is a fine show flower, and even the smaller flowers of less temperate climates develop wonderfully if cut in the bud and brought indoors. They last long and are as white as a Snowdrop.

'Acolyte', from Lanarth, is a better grower with larger flowers generally two to a stem, and one of the best white 5*b* forms.

'Alys', an Engleheart seedling, I place very high. The cup widens out in a pleasing line. Three good forms sent to me from Ireland are 'Blanc Souffre', slightly tinted with sulphur, with long, narrow segments making a very graceful flower; 'Blanc de Neige', much like 'Venetia', has a beautifully green tube and the flower stands out horizontally; and 'Blanc Jaunâtre', a strong grower, is twin-flowered and hangs its head at a pleasing angle.

'Dawn' is my favourite Daffodil, both for cutting and planting on ledges of the rock garden. It appeared unexpectedly in a bed of Mr. Engleheart's seedlings. Its pure white reflexing perianth and pendent poise proclaim triandrus parentage, but what gave it a corona as flat and as golden as a guinea no one knows. Possibly it is poeticus influence, but there is no trace of a red rim and no poeticus has so flat an eye. The flowers come in pairs and their white segments intermingle and interfere with one another slightly, which causes them to stand out here and there and look like the wings of three white butterflies dancing on a couple of large buttercups.

Nothing very much like it has been raised since. The nearest approach is Mr. Chapman's ' Bracken ', a more robust plant, very beautiful in form but not so bright in colouring as the daintier, more slender ' Dawn '.

' Silver Chimes ', a triandrus and Tazetta cross, is another plant of outstanding refinement and charm. It was raised by Mr. E. Martin in Cornwall and received an award for cutting in 1922. It has all the beauty and rich effect of the best Tazettas combined with a refinement of texture and colouring not found in any of them. The whiteness of triandrus is at its best in the perianth, and has also toned down the lemon of the corona to a citron tint as clear as the light of an evening sky.

It is a strong grower, and so far it has done well here, though away from its mild western birthplace; but then it has been given the most sheltered corners that can be found, and certainly deserves them. As a pot plant it is superb, the very dark, broad leaves showing up the glistening purity of the many-flowered heads.

XIII

CYCLAMINEUS

THE R.H.S. Division VI. being intended chiefly for show purposes, *N. cyclamineus* itself was included in Division XI., which is well named various. Here it shall preside as the head of its family. Its interesting history has more plot in it than the mere confusion of names and portraits common to that of other species. It includes not only the total disappearance of the hero for some two and a half centuries, but the statement by Dean Herbert, one of the greatest authorities, that ' it is an absurdity which will never be found to exist '.

He also blundered sadly in attributing the excellent portrait of its unmistakable features to Rudbeck, instead of to the unknown author of the *Theatrum Florae*, on Pl. 20 of which he saw the figure.

It is easy to imagine how this arose and to forgive him. He had been examining Olaf Rudbeck's horrible figures in the *Campi Elysii* and citing some of them on p. 305 of his *Amaryllidaceae*, and evidently was displeased with them, for he wrote, ' no reliance can be placed on such a figure '. Feeling thus about Rudbeck's vile copies of older figures, he regarded that of the *Theatrum* as of like value. A slip of the pen substituted Rudbeck as the author, and he dismissed it in these words: ' Looking at the rest of Rudbeck' figures I have no hesitation in rejecting it as a non-entity.'

Thus it would have been the parallel of the Tichborne claimant in fact and Mrs. Harris in fiction, had not Messrs. Tait and Schmitz rediscovered it near Oporto in 1885.

The name N. cyclamineus is correctly attributed to
De Candolle in the Index Kewensis. He so named it
in the list of species given under Pl. 486, the last of
all the beautiful illustrations by Redouté in *Les Liliacées*.
De Candolle gave no description, but cited the figure
in t. 20 of the *Theatrum Florae*, N. hispanicus minor
luteus, amplo calyce, foliis reflexis.

Haworth used the name in his *Monograph*, but was
not the first to name it as stated in the *Botanical
Magazine* under t. 6950 in 1887. This figure is not
very good; the flowers are somewhat conventionalised
and have lost the charm of the neat living bloom with
its wide-awake expression rather like that of a kicking
horse with its ears laid back. N. cyclamineus differs
from all Ajax forms in its narrow cylindrical corona,
generally longer than the sharply reflexed segments.
It has narrow, deep green leaves and brilliantly yellow
flowers with the corona a little deeper in colour than
the perianth.

It is one of the earliest to begin flowering and because of its firm texture lasts in good condition for a
long period. Though difficult to grow well and effectively in ordinary beds, it is a most attractive plant in
ground that is little interfered with, especially in light,
rather moist soil, where it will sow itself freely and
form colonies.

The drifts of its gay flowers rising from green moss
or thin grass as may be seen at Wisley should inspire
any gardener who has patience and a similar situation
to plant and sow and watch over cyclamineus, until he
gains a corresponding reward.

As a parent cyclamineus has produced some very
distinct forms. To my thinking the smaller are
the better. Crossed with asturiensis (minimus) some
dainty little plants suitable for rock gardens have been
raised, and others have appeared spontaneously where
these species have met. One raised by Mr. Chapman

called minicycla gained an Award of Merit, and was figured in *The Garden*, Feb. 8th, 1913.

With larger trumpets the crosses have produced somewhat ungainly flowers; the narrowing of the trumpet in a large flower is not always pleasing, and with reflexing segments looks snoutish. Barr's 'Golden Arrow' is saved by its spreading mouth and the wing-like poise of its perianth segments.

'Golden Cycle', raised by Captain Hawker, is a bright and early flower, rather too dwarf for its long corona. Mrs. Backhouse's 'Little Witch' has a pleasantly fluted cup. 'Pepys', raised by Mr. P. D. Williams, is remarkable in that it is a bicolor with pale lemon perianth and rich yellow tubular crown.

'Orange Glory' has a distinctly red-orange trumpet with a well-toothed rim; a light yellow, twisting but scarcely reflexing perianth and a rather strong Van Sion type of scent. The anthers have the brown tips that suggest maximus or some other hispanicus form in its pedigree. Its neat flowers last in good condition for a long period, and it is very pleasing as a pot plant. 'February Gold' is a similar but smaller early-flowering form.

'Beryl' was raised by Mr. P. D. Williams, and having poeticus as one parent it has inherited rounded, overlapping perianth segments which open yellow and grow paler as they age until they are almost white. They reflex only slightly, as their width prevents their turning back, and the flowers look downwards but otherwise show little trace of cyclamineus, as the corona is short, of medium cadmium yellow for main colour, but broadly edged with orange inside and out. It is a particularly charming rock garden plant and good to pick for small vases.

XIV

The Jonquil Group

THE JONQUILS or Rush-leaved Daffodils form a group easily distinguished from every other by their deep green, round or semicylindrical leaves, in association with flowers having short cups.

Four types are sufficiently outstanding to be regarded as species. Others which vary greatly and grade into one another may be reckoned as varieties or subspecies connected with two of these four, and yet others are hybrids with plants belonging to other groups. They can be arranged thus:

A. *Plants dwarf, leaves filiform, round or semicylindrical.*

(1) Flowers solitary, white	Watieri
(2) Flowers one to five, yellow	juncifolius
variety 1, corona six-lobed	var. rupicola
variety 2, flowers four to six, pale	var. gaditanus
subspecies *a*, tube distinctly	
curved, flowers very small	minutiflorus
subspecies *β*, tube slightly curved,	
corona cup-shaped, orange	scaberulus

B. *Plants tall.*

(*a*) Leaves slender, $\frac{1}{5}$ to $\frac{1}{8}$ inch wide.

(1) Corona short, spreading	Jonquilla
(2) Corona cup-shaped	jonquilloides

(*b*) Leaves $\frac{1}{8}$ inch wide or more, of hybrid origin.

(1) Corona long	odorus
(2) Corona short	intermedius
(3) Corona flat, tall	gracilis
(4) Corona flat, shorter and smaller	tenuior

N. Watieri, the only white-flowered species of this group, was described by Dr. Maire in the *Bulletin Soc. Hist. Nat. de l'Afrique du Nord*, vol. xii., p. 186, and named after M. Watier, who discovered it on Mount Yagour near Mesfiona in the Great Atlas. It resembles N. juncifolius in size and appearance, differing in the flower being pure white throughout, and from N. dubius in having only one flower to a scape.

It was introduced to Britain by Mr. G. P. Baker, who cultivates it successfully in the open ground and in a frame and has generously distributed seeds. It promises to become a precious plant for the rock garden and Alpine house, being only 4 inches in height with very narrow, slightly channelled leaves, and is apparently hardy.

The flower is about 1 inch in diameter, absolutely snow-white in perianth and corona, and of an exquisitely crystalline texture shown up by the contrast of its long green perianth tube. There is a drawing of it in *Gardening Illustrated* for May 30th, 1931, p. 347.

N. juncifolius was so named by Requien in Lagasca's *Gen. and Spec.*, November, 1816, and by Loiseleur in *Mem. Soc. Linn.*, *Paris*, 1827. It is an unfortunate though apt name, as it was used by many early writers for most of the other narrow-leaved species, for which Tabernaemontanus, Lobel and Clusius used the same woodcuts accredited to differently named plants.

The only one resembling Lagasca's plant is used by Lobel in the Latin and German Editions of his work and his volume of figures, as juncifolius flore rotundae circinatis roseo and in Johnson's Gerard for juncifolius Roseoluteus, described there as ' yellow or else white '. Clusius, Parkinson and Linnæus do not mention it.

Haworth's Philogyne minor seems intended for it,

but, excepting N. rupicola Schultes, the synonyms
cited belong elsewhere, and it is one of those he marks
with an asterisk to show he had not seen a specimen.

The best figure is t. xciv. in Willkomm's *Illustrationes Florae Hispaniae*, 1881-85, where two forms
are represented as A. vulgaris and an unusually
tall form with three to five flowers as B. major.
Burbidge's Pl. 27 shows long- and short-leaved specimens, and Herbert's Fig. 21, Pl. 39, a single bloom
and tip of a leaf. *Gardening Illustrated*, December 5th,
1931, p. 939, has a photograph of growing plants,
and in the Abbé Coste's *Flore de France* Fig. 3547 is
a good line-drawing. N. juncifolius is mostly found
in the mountains in Spain, Portugal, France and
Corsica. It colours meadowland, as buttercups do
with us, in some parts of the Pyrenees, especially near
Gèdres, and also grows into matted clumps on rocky
ledges. In the Bouches du Rhône it occurs in stony
ground on the limestone hills near St. Rémy. In the
garden it prefers well-drained gritty soil in open
sunny places. With its brilliantly yellow, well-formed
flowers, delicious scent and neat habit it is very desirable for a rock garden, or for pans in an Alpine house.
The tiny rush-like leaves could never deserve Farrer's
indictment of Narcissi as dying so untidily—' in
flopping masses of yellow decay '.

N. gaditanus of Boissier differs in having longer,
twisted leaves, more flowers to a spathe, sometimes as
many as five, a curved tube and pedicels of unequal
length. It grows on bushy slopes in Algarve in Southern
Portugal and in the southernmost corner of Andalusia
near Jerez and between Cichlana and Medina-Sidonia.
Coming from such southern situations it requires
thorough and careful ripening, and cultivation in
pans in a cool house would most likely be the only
method to ensure success. Burbidge's Fig. C on
Pl. 27 shows that it would be worth growing.

N. rupicola was described as a species by Dufour
in Roemer and Schultes, *Systema Vegetabilium*, vol. vii.,
p. 958, in 1830, and again by Willkomm and Lange
in the *Prodromus Fl. Hispaniae*, vol. i., p.152, 1870.
It differs from N. juncifolius chiefly in having solitary
flowers almost sessile on the scape, while in juncifolius the pedicels are ½ to 1½ inches in length and the
flowers one to four. Again in rupicola the corona is
more or less six-lobed, and in extreme forms the lobes
spread out nearly flat, but in others with wide perianth
segments the corona is almost as in the typical juncifolius.

The ovary is described as longer than broad and
boat-shaped, and the style is shorter in rupicola than
in juncifolius, which has a round ovary. These characters distinguish it as a subspecies at most. It is
found in crevices of granitic rocks in Tarragona in
Spain and the Serra d'Estrella in Central Portugal,
so high that the flowering season is as late as June.

Boissier describes it as N. apodanthus. It is figured
in the *Bot. Mag.*, t. 6473, C, in Graells' *Ramil-
lettes de Plantas Españolas*, vol. i., p. 17, t. 7, and
in *The Gardeners' Chronicle*, May 11th, 1929, by
photographs of two distinct forms.

N. scaberulus is described by Henriques in Bolet.
Soc. Brot., vi., 1888, p. 45, and in *The Gardeners'
Chronicle*, 1888, ii., p. 296. This is a very local
form found only in Portugal high on a granitic mountain
near Oliviera do Conde in moist gravel. It resembles
N. rupicola, but its flowers are even smaller, only ½ inch
across, and of a deeper orange colouring, especially
in the corona, which is large for so small a flower.
The tube is slightly curved, the leaves produced in
pairs. The scape has six conspicuous ridges which,
like the margins of the leaves, are furnished with
minute, colourless teeth, pointing downwards and producing the slight roughness to the touch that is the

justification for the name. It has been grown and shown in pans by Dr. Giuseppi, who has lately visited its home and introduced it to cultivation.

N. minutiflorus is described by Willkomm in *Bot. Zeit.*, xviii., 104 (1860), and *Illustrationes Florae Hispaniae*, vol. 1., p. 122, and figured in t. 74, B. It must surely bear the smallest flowers of the genus, as the tube is only 10 mm. long and the perianth segments 4 mm. Like gaditanus it bears four or more flowers with curved tubes—but very much smaller, and a style much shorter than the tube, whereas that of gaditanus is extended beyond the throat.

It seems to be the same as Queltia pusilla of Herbert, described in his *Amaryllidaceae*, p. 315 (1837), from a specimen in Banks's herbarium gathered by Masson between Ayamonte and Huelba in Spain. Herbert's Pl. 43, Fig. 22 (given as Fig. 2 in the text), represents it clearly.

N. pusillus G. Don in Loudon's Hort. Brit., 116, is juncifolius.

N. Jonquilla, named by Linnæus in the First Edition of *Species Plantarum*, was defined as ' foliis subulatis ' to distinguish it from Tazetta with ' foliis planis '. He cites Bauhin's N. juncifolius luteus minor, *Pinax*, p. 51, and N. j. minor and 2 of Clusius's *Historia* with a wrong reference, i., p. 60, for ii., p. 159. Willkomm considers that Clusius's juncifolius 2 is Jonquilla and his juncifolius minor is jonquilloides.

Haworth used the name for a genus with four species, three of which he arranged after the manner of The Three Bears of nursery fame as major, media and minor, following Parkinson. Parkinson has a figure for the first only, a seven-flowered head of small, starry flowers, somewhat like Burbidge's Fig. C on Pl. 27 of N. gaditanus or Webbii. It is a poor figure, and if it represents any plant at all faithfully, it is not a form to be desired. Parkinson's description applies to N. Jonquilla better than his figure does.

Herbert places it with N. odorus and juncifolius in Queltia, the rightful home for N. incomparabilis, but he has doubts about it owing to its peculiar seed, and notes its likeness to the autumnal species in having so long and slender a tube and erect capsules. N. Jonquilla is a well-marked species undoubtedly spontaneous in Spain and Portugal, where it is abundant in mountain meadows, and has a wide range in Southern Europe as a naturalised plant in suitable ground. It also occurs in the Balearic Isles and North Africa.

It stands out clearly among related forms owing to certain well-marked characters. Such are the dark, rush-like leaves over a foot in height, slightly channelled on the upper surface, the slender, round scape bearing from two to six deep yellow flowers with saucer-shaped coronas and long, straight tubes, and the strongest fragrance of the genus, surpassing that of the poeticus varieties. Two or three heads of Jonquil will scent a large room and may prove unpleasantly strong when used on a dinner table. De Candolle in *Les Liliacées* says it is dangerous for nervous people and should not be placed in closed rooms. It is an old garden favourite and can be left alone for many years if planted in sheltered but sunny borders.

Its double form is known as ' Queen Anne's Jonquil ' and is Parkinson's N. juncifolius flore pleno of his good Fig. 8, p. 93. Clusius's block on p. 13 of the *Curae Posteriores*, used again by Johnson in his edition of Gerard, is not so good, but, as Clusius tells us, it was drawn from a coloured picture and notes sent by Matthæus Caccini, who had but one plant of it in his garden at Florence. Burbidge's Fig. C on Pl. 40. gives a good idea of this charming but uncommon form with its successions of perianth segments and small divided lobes of the corona.

Although so frequently grown in gardens, Jonquilla has varied but little. Parkinson wrote of a form with ' a line or strake of white ' in the middle of every perianth segment, possibly a freak or the result of some injury. A form collected in Spain is smaller than the old garden plant, paler in colour with a six-lobed corona.

There are many good figures of N. Jonquilla, among which is *Bot. Mag.* t. 15. Redouté's in *Les Liliacées*, t. 159, is very good. In vol. ix., t. 366, of Reichenbach's *Flora germanica* the segments are long and too much pointed. Burbidge's Fig. A on Pl. 40; Moon's in *The Garden*, vol. xxxii., Pl. 620, 1887; and Coste's in *Fl. de France*, 3548, are accurate portraits.

N. jonquilloides was described by Willkomm in *Bot. Zeit.*, p. 103, in 1860. He considers it to be the plant Clusius described as juncifolius minor in the *Historia*, Lib. ii., p. 159, which Linnæus cites for Jonquilla as well as the preceding plant on the same page. Clusius described the minor form as more slender with rounder leaves, yellow flowers scented like the former, but with firmer and much more orbiculate segments.

Willkomm makes it differ from Jonquilla by its smaller bulb, narrower leaves shorter than the scape, pedicels longer than the spathe and smaller flowers, but especially by a corona nearly as long as the perianth segments, and as flowering in January and February, whereas Jonquilla in dry lowland, where it is scarce, only flowers in the end of February and in March, and in mountain regions, where it is more frequent, in March and April.

The block used by Clusius shows a flat corona and rather long segments, but as it is the same that Lobel used for juncifolius serotinus we need not place much reliance on its having been drawn from the plants it was afterwards used to illustrate.

Willkomm records it from between Monchique and Lagos in Algarve, where it was plentiful in marshy ground. His t. 38 in the *Illustrationes* (1881) shows a five-flowered head of small flowers with yellow perianths and orange coronas as strongly coloured as those of a ' Soleil d'Or ' Tazetta. The tall stalk and lengthy perianth tube seem out of proportion for the shapely little flowers, which with the richly coloured cup-shaped coronas would be very attractive on a dwarf plant.

N. odorus, as described by Linnæus in the Second Edition of *Species Plantarum*, has been accepted as the correct name for a group of slightly varying plants which have been a source of confusion to many. Linnæus, usually so chary of giving names to any but widely differing plants, has in this case bestowed the three names odorus, calathinus and trilobus on what are now recognised as varieties of one plant.

Salisbury provided a generic name Philogyne for this trinity in unity, and Haworth contrived to furnish it with nine species and four varieties. Gawler pointed out under N. calathinus, t. 934 of the *Botanical Magazine*, 1806, that Linnæus had confused odorus as described in the ' Amaenitates Academicae ' with N. incomparabilis, but in citing that work for the odorus of the Second Edition of *Species Plantarum* he changed his description and synonym.

Herbert was the first to clear up the confusion in his *Amaryllidaceae*, p. 313, in 1837. He decided that Linnæus never had a specimen with a corona of the same length as the perianth, as he defines his calathinus. Herbert wrote: ' He named it in MS. on the margin of the First Edition, and published it in the Second with a reference to Clusius' No. 1 juncif. 9 and Rudb. El. 2, p. 60, f. 5. Rudbeck's figure is a very unfaithful copy of that of Clusius with a reference to it, therefore the original plant of Clusius is the thing meant, and that corresponds very closely with N. calathinus *Bot. Mag.* Rudbeck exaggerated the size of the cup in his engraving, on the faith of which Linnæus described it as having the cup and limb nearly equal, but no specimen has ever been forthcoming.'

Linnæus's herbarium contains a two-flowered specimen as N. odorus from the Upsala Garden, which agrees with his description ' flos luteus, triplo major flore N. Tazettae . . . nectario non fimbriato sed ore diviso lobis 6 obtusis '. So Herbert selected odorus for the specific name to cover seven varieties and two sub-varieties, a testimony to the variation to be found in this race.

The question then arises as to the nature of this variable species. Is it a natural species or a hybrid ? Burbidge describes its appearance as intermediate between N. Jonquilla and incomparabilis. The late Mr. Peter Barr wrote that by some it was supposed to be a hybrid between Jonquilla and Pseudo-Narcissus, but he would not like to stake his reputation on this. No wild habitat is known, and he failed to find a trace of it in Portugal. Coste limits its occurrence to fields and meadows in France. Willkomm records trilobus as found in meadows in Southern Spain ' according to Salisbury ', but places odorus among the forms whose occurrence in Spain is questionable. Nyman's *Conspectus* gives for localities Portugal and France, and queries its occurrence in Spain, adding that this species is often cultivated and sometimes occurs subspontaneously. If a set of intermediates appeared spontaneously in some locality where Jonquilla and an Ajax grew together, those that were larger than the Jonquil parent and of a deeper yellow than the Ajax would be easily distinguished and likely to be collected for cultivation.

Clusius first saw it in 1595 at the Leyden Academy Garden. Crispin de Pas in *Hortus Floridus* gives beautiful figures of three varieties on Pls. 23 and 24; one of these is the double Campernelle and the others represent heminalis and rugulosus. Parkinson figures two single forms and a double one.

It has been cultivated over a long period, and Salisbury wrote in 1812 of its being sold in Covent Garden in nosegays. Several varieties are still grown in gardens and correspond for the most part with those named and figured in the last century.

Odorus itself goes by the name of the Campernelle Jonquil. The question has been raised as to the spelling of this name, and suggestions have been made that it should be changed to Campanelle, as though from the Italian campanello, meaning 'a little bell'. The Italian name for the plant is Giunchiglione, however, and Campanelle is the common name for Convolvulus.

Haworth used the name Campernelli for a plant he called 'The Late great 6-lobed', which, according to him, was a later-flowering variety of odorus and 'N. Campernelli Hortulanorum'. This suggests that it was grown in gardens under that name, which was formed as though to connect it with some man whose name was Campernell and of whom no record has yet been found. Donn in *Hortus Cantabrigensis* gives 'N. Campernelli Campernell's Narcissus', but may have been merely translating Haworth's name without knowledge of anyone bearing it. Herbert, one of the most meticulous of writers as regards names, used it as Campernelliana, also regarding it as an honorific name derived from that of a person.

It remained in unchallenged usage until 1909, when the modern version Campanelle appeared in a trade list, and there is no known prior use of that form in other literature. The usage as to the nomenclature of plants is that, unless there is indubitable evidence that a printer's error has occurred, it is not permissible to alter the spelling of a name that has been effectively published. So Haworth's spelling must stand whatever may be its origin, but, as he used it for a pale, late-flowering form that cannot be identified at the present time, it would be best to drop the Latin form until the rediscovery of that variety. The English form Campernelle has been in constant use for so long for typical N. odorus that, however desirable it might be to use none but Linnæus's scientific name, the change is unlikely to become general.

The best figure of the typical odorus is Redouté's t. 157 in *Les Liliacées*, showing a two-flowered specimen. The *Bot. Mag.* t. 78, though rather small, is a good representation.

Salisbury called it N. laetus and Haworth Philogyne Curtisii. Burbidge's Pl. 23 shows two forms differing in the length of the corona. His note to this plate states: ' This plant is very variable in colour and size of flower '.

In Coste's *Fl. de France*, Fig. 3550, with syn. N. laetus Salisb., shows the shorter-cupped form very clearly. Moon's brilliantly coloured drawing in *The Garden*, vol. xxxii., 1887, Pl. 620, is excellent.

N. odorus rugulosus is the largest variety and in a garden form known as maximus is of a uniform orange yellow. Burbidge's Pl. 25 A shows the usual form with its characteristic pleated mouth of the corona. Parkinson's Fig. 5, p. 89, fits this form.

Heminalis is a name given by Salisbury from the Greek hēmina, a measure holding half of the hecteus, the Latin sextarius, either in allusion to the length or the shape of the corona. Parkinson's Fig. 4, p. 93, the yellow junquillia with a great cup, was recognised by Haworth as this, and he called it the ' narrow-cupped '. Burbidge's Pl. 24 shows it as a middle-sized form of very deep colouring similar to the *Bot. Mag.* t. 934. The plant now listed as aurantiacus and ' Orange Queen ' agrees with it and is the deepest in colour of all Jonquils.

Burbidge's var. minor (B on his Pl. 25) I have not seen. It is a neat, small-flowered form which would be a pleasant plant for rock gardens. Perhaps it is still grown in some old gardens in Ireland. Redouté's Pl. 428 in *Les Liliacées* as N. laetus may represent this form.

The double form is listed as Double Campernelle and rugulosus flore pleno. It is Parkinson's Fig. 7 of p. 93 and Burbidge's Pl. 26, a very pleasant garden plant, not too strongly scented and lasting well as a cut flower.

All the Jonquils are worth growing where well-drained but deep soil can be spared to them in a sheltered position, where they can get all the best of the sunshine.

N. intermedius, described by Loiseleur in *Flora Gallica*, i., 236, t. 6, is so markedly intermediate in its characters between N. Tazetta and Jonquilla that it is most likely a natural hybrid between the two species. The leaves are semicylindrical with a deep channel in the upper face and of a lustrous, dark green, very lengthy (a foot or more) and $\frac{3}{8}$ to $\frac{1}{2}$ inch wide in their lower half. The flowers are from three to ten in a head with the perianth segments paler then in Jonquilla, longer and more pointed; the corona is short with a waved edge, and deeper in colour than the segments. The perianth tube is unusually long, approaching an inch in length, very slender and frequently curved. The scent is strong but not so heavy as that of Jonquilla. It was said to be plentiful near Bayonne and Dax in the Basses Pyrenees. Willkomm includes it as bifrons and primulinus in the *Prodromus Florae Hispanicae*, but only on the authority of Gawler and Haworth. Nyman adds near Pegli in Italy, and Moggridge gathered it near Mentone. Possibly its history is a parallel with that of N. odorus, but with Tazetta as one parent instead of an Ajax.

Moggridge's Pl. 40 is good, but like others of his rather weak in colour. T. 1186 of the *Botanical Magazine* is very good. Gawler calls it 'bifrons' from an almost equally proportioned resemblance to both Jonquilla and 'calathinus', the latter being N. odorus. He wrote: 'Is it a mule production between these two species?' His plants were imported from Holland and bore leaves nearly 2 feet long.

Redouté's Pl. 459 in vol. 8 of *Les Liliacées* as N. radiatus shows a two-flowered specimen with rather wide but pointed segments. Haworth made this into his Hermione compressa, the Jasmine Jonquil (*Mon.*, p. 7, xiii., 3).

A larger form with a darker corona cut into six rounded lobes is shown in t. 1299 of the *Botanical Magazine* as N. bifrons β, and Gawler says it represents bifrons when newly imported from Holland, which after several years of cultivation in our gardens becomes the smaller form figured in t. 1186. Haworth calls this larger form H. primulina, the Cowslip-cupped, a pretty allusion to the orange cup, and adds yet another of his imaginary species as H. biscrenata, of greater stature, more numerous flowers and the six lobes of the cup divided into twelve parts. This suggests no more than a condition resulting from better cultivation.

Burbidge's Pl. 38 shows the type and bifrons, but not very well as compared with the *Botanical Magazine* figures. Coste's Fig. 3589 is good, but the leaves are not represented as sufficiently large.

N. intermedius is too seldom seen in gardens, being graceful, fragrant and early flowering. A larger plant with a bright orange cup was listed as N. intermedius 'Sunset', but looks as though it were a seedling with the influence of some Barrii form added.

There are plants with narrow leaves that have been associated with the Jonquils and the origin of which is unknown. They are possibly hybrids with N. Jonquilla as one parent. One of these is N. *trilobus*, as figured in the *Bot. Mag.*, t. 945. Gawler in the text writes that it was sent to him by Haworth as N. nutans, and there seems little reason for his associating it with Linnæus's trilobus of the Second Edition of *Species Plantarum*, except that Linnæus cites N. angustifolius pallidus calyce flavo of Bauhin's *Pinax*, p. 51. Gawler himself considered it an 'unlucky name' for a plant less conspicuously trilobate than many others of this genus, and that it was intermediate between Jonquilla and triandrus. Haworth in his *Monograph*, p. 4, placed it as Ganymedes nutans, citing the *Botanical Magazine* figure, and Herbert corroborated this. It might well be a Jonquilla and triandrus cross, but is not known in cultivation at the present time.

N. *gracilis* is described in the *Botanical Register* in 1824 under t. 816 from Sabine's MSS., followed by an account of the plant by Dr. Lindley. The leaves are like those of Jonquilla and the flowers much like poeticus, but the lower stamens do not reach to the throat as in that group. The perianth is about 2 inches in diameter with overlapping segments of a soft creamy yellow tint, the short-cupped corona of a darker yellow shade. The tall, slender stems bear two or three flowers which are at their best in the latter half of May, being the latest to flower of the yellow forms of Narcissus.

Gracilis is not found in a wild state, and is perhaps a cross between Jonquilla and biflorus or some small form of poeticus. Other good figures are Sweet's *British Flower Garden*, Second Series, vol. ii., t. 136, Redouté's in *Les Liliacées*, 427, under the name of N. intermedius, and Burbidge's A on Pl. 37. It is a charmingly refined plant, but requires care and a

10

sheltered position to prevent its dying out in the average English garden.

N. tenuior owes its name and description to W. Curtis, who published it in 1797 along with a beautiful figure in the *Bot. Mag.*, vol. xi., t. 379. Much like N. gracilis in shape and colour, it is smaller in all its parts, with paler perianth when fresh, and becomes nearly white as the flowers mature.

Its origin is an unsolved mystery. Curtis found it at Walworth in the garden of James Maddock, the author of the *Florists' Directory*, who had obtained the bulbs from Holland under the name N. flore sulphureo junquifolius, most of which were ' in a double state '.

Salisbury in *Trans. Hort. Soc.* 1812 renamed it Helena tegulaeflora and declared that it grew wild and was the plant sent to Clusius by Venerius from Rovergue (that is Bordeaux), mentioned in the Appendix to Clusius's *Historia*, p. 257. Clusius, however, in *Curae Posteriores*, p. 12, connects Venerius's plant with his N. juncifolius minor of the *Historia*, which is either Jonquilla or jonquilloides. This wild guess of Salisbury's is repeated in Baker's *Amaryllideae*. Burbidge shows a yellow and a nearly white form of tenuior on his Pl. 37 B. It is a scarce plant now and more difficult than gracilis to keep in health. The double form mentioned by Curtis has not been seen since he wrote.

N. Jonquilla has been used very successfully as a pollen parent by Mr. Engleheart, Mr. P. D. Williams and others, and a fine race of garden plants has been produced. Their dark, upright, narrow leaves are very pleasing as compared with the wide, massive foliage of other groups. Additional good features are tall scapes bearing two or three flowers which open in succession, the fine, smooth texture of their wide and beautifully rounded perianths, and above all other qualities they remain fresh and fragrant for a longer period than most others. These hybrids, with odorus and others, form Section VII. of the R.H.S. Classification.

' Buttercup ' dates from 1890 and was one of the first to become popular. It was found in a bed of mixed seedlings raised by Mr. Engleheart, but after they had been sold. ' Pilgrim ', a pale bicoloured incomparabilis, was another good plant from that bed. When well grown ' Buttercup ' is a fine upstanding plant, with one-flowered scapes, self-coloured, pure yellow flowers with perianth 3 inches in diameter and the corona as long as the segments. De Graaff's ' Golden Sceptre ' is a very similar form; its longer and narrower perianth tubes and ovaries are the chief characters that distinguish it. Both are strongly scented and good for cutting. ' Lanarth ' is one of the strongest growers of Mr. Williams's set; it frequently carries two flowers to the head, the cup is flat and is strongly tinted with orange when at its best. It received the Award of Garden Merit in 1930 after trial at Wisley.

' Trevithian ' is easily recognised by its Cornish name as another of Mr. Williams's raising. Rather paler in colouring and with a perianth of longer, waved segments, it has the look of an incomparabilis at first sight, but has inherited the superb texture and fragrance of Jonquilla. A robust habit and its two-flowered scapes make it a good garden plant.

' Hesla ', from the same stud, has a larger, flatter flower, with short open cup waved at its edge and not much deeper in colour than the pale yellow perianth. ' Polmesk ' is larger and paler than ' Hesla ', standing up with a stem of 20 inches and bearing a flower $3\frac{1}{2}$ inches in diameter, a wonderful achievement for a plant of Jonquilla descent. The outer segments are broad and flat, while the inner are pleasingly narrowed or clawed at the base with rolled-in edges and are slightly set forward, giving a cheerful, wide-awake expression to this very fine primrose-coloured flower with a prettily fluted short cup.

'Penpol' is another giant and bears two or three flowers to a stem. They have flat perianths and large open cups of a very bright yellow, deeper in colour than those of the two last, but the perianth is rather ribby in texture.

One still under number has a stem measuring 20 inches from ground to ovary and large, deep yellow flowers like a magnified odorus, which it resembles in having a long, lobed cup with straight sides. The colour of the backs of the segments is deeper than on the inner face, so it stands out conspicuously as a remarkably dark flower.

Pale primrose perianths of many shades have appeared, some with almost self-coloured flat cups, others with lobed cups edged with orange, and some with very bright or dark yellow perianths have cups as red as that of 'Fortune'. The most remarkable is one with a white perianth of beautiful form and a flat citron cup with crinkled edge rimmed with yellow, set on the long green tube of a Jonquil.

The foundation of this strain was laid by crossing the Barrii 'Pilgrim' with Jonquilla. N. odorus has proved useless as a parent as its pollen is dry and ineffective. More than a score of Jonquil hybrids have been registered, but too few have as yet found their way into gardens and to the shows.

'Golden Goblet' is, up to the present, the only known instance of a secondary cross between a Jonquilla hybrid and an Ajax. It bears a large yellow flower of good substance and form.

'Solleret' received its A.M. in 1929 and provided the winning flower in the class for Jonquil hybrids in the 1934 R.H.S. Daffodil Show. It was raised by Mr. Engleheart and has a large bold flower of remarkably deep yellow colouring. Good figures can be found in *Gard. Chron.* and *Gardening Illustrated* for April 27th, 1929, showing it with a single-flowered scape. 'Beauregard' (Barr), well figured in Mr. Calvert's book, shows the other type with three flowers to a head. The next page (177) shows a solitary bloom of Lanarth, a twin-flowered variety when growing strongly. St. Ruan also runs to twins when well grown, and its primrose-tinted flowers look well in the bolder portions of a rock-garden. Anyone looking out for a distinct class of Narcissus to plant as a contrast to the wide-leaved, large-flowered Trumpet and Leedsii forms would do well to plant these Jonquil hybrids, placed rather thinly so that the full value of their slender leaves and gracefully poised flowers may stand out clearly among the sturdy figures of their neighbours.

XV

TAZETTA

IN THE *Species Plantarum* of 1753 Linnæus described
Tazetta as 'spatha multiflora, nectario campanulato,
foliis planis'. This terse description was sufficient
for his purpose of pointing out the distinctions between
the six plants which he then considered the only species
of the genus. The many-flowered spathe divided
Tazetta and Jonquilla from the others, because Linnæus
was unaware of the occasional occurrence of more
than one flower in serotinus, while the flat leaves of
Tazetta contrasted with the awl-shaped (subulate)
leaves of Jonquilla.

This is characteristic of Linnæus's methods as a
lumper, and did not arise from a lack of knowledge
of the many forms cultivated in Holland. In his
note in the *Hortus Cliffortianus*, the work he compiled
while in charge of Dr. Georg Clifford's garden near
Haarlem, he wrote of N. Tazetta: 'It varies in the
size of the flowers, in colour, being white or yellow in
nectary (i.e., the cup) or petals or both, in varying
doubleness, the size or shape of the cup and the number
of flowers from each spathe.'

For contrast take Burbidge's note: 'This plant has
been irreverently styled the "Dustbin" or "Scape
Goat" of the genus, on account of its protean variability, just as the ubiquitous Euphorbiaceae is frequently made a temporary refuge for all undeterminable
species of other natural orders.'

Salisbury invented the genus Hermione, named
after the daughter of Menelaus and Helen, publishing
it in vol. I of the *Transactions of the Horticultural*

Society in 1812, but gave the name only, without distinguishing characters. He made it include as species N. Jonquilla, juncifolius, intermedius, schizanthes, tenuior and six others which are the only ones we should now class as Tazetta forms. These are H. leucoifolia (perhaps 'Scilly White'), stylosa (italicus), jasminea (papyraceus), cupularis ('Soleil d'Or'), floribunda (perhaps 'Grand Monarque'), and crenularis (Bazelman major).

Haworth adopted the name Hermione and supplied generic characters, but of such a nature that Herbert declares they are 'founded on trivial features in some cases unfit even to support a specific distinction'.

Haworth, according to his usual practice, furnished the genus with fifty-four species, many of which are no more than garden forms. He did good service, however, by arranging them in three sections according to their colouring. In this he followed Linnæus's extended definition of Tazetta given in the Second Edition of *Species Plantarum*, but confused matters by further divisions governed by the comparative proportions of segments and corona.

Herbert laid more stress on the length of tube in relation to that of limb, which, however, brings together plants too divergent in colour and general appearance to seem naturally grouped.

J. G. Baker's classification in the *Handbook of Amaryllideae* will be found the simplest and most convenient. He gives three series according to coloration:

Series I. Tazettinae bicolores, perianth white, corona yellow.

Series II. T. albae, perianth and corona both white.

Series III. T. luteae, perianth and corona both yellow.

Tazettinae. Series I. bicolores. This series can be subdivided into Sections *a* and *b*, corona orange, corona pale yellow.

Section *a.* *N. Tazetta* of Linnæus has the widest geographical distribution of any species of Narcissus, extending from the coast of Northern Spain, through Portugal and the Mediterranean regions of Southern Europe and North Africa, to Syria, Asia Minor, Persia and Kashmir, and even as far as China and Japan.

Naturally with such a range many local varieties occur, differing in size and shape from the narrow-cupped form with reflexing limb that is Herbert's corcyrensis, to N. elatus, Pl. 70, Fig. A, of Bicknell's *Flowering Plants of the Riviera* with flowers over 2 inches in breadth and wide-open cups.

The form most frequently found is that figured by Moggridge in *Contributions to the Flora of Mentone*, Pl. 23. In this the limb is not pure white, having a slight yellowish tint, and the cup is of a deep orange colour. Where found it is generally very plentiful, especially in olive-terraces and vineyards in Spain, France and Italy, but occasionally in moist meadows. It is certainly either the Narcissus or the Leirion of Theophrastus mentioned as appearing in Spring after the Leucoion in the list of coronary flowers.

I have seen it growing in Greece far from cultivation in low-lying, moist ground. Like Anemone coronaria and pavonina, Hyacinthus orientalis, Iris albicans and Tulipa Clusiana, it is possible that such a fragrant and easily grown plant may owe its wide distribution to human agency, and that like them it is of Eastern origin. Plants which establish themselves freely in cultivated ground, and are chiefly propagated by divisions of the roots in ploughing or hoeing, and which seldom seed or show minor variations among the mass, may frequently be regarded as clones. That is to say, they are the produce of an individual root which has strayed into congenial environment. We know that Iris albicans has been mainly distributed by Moslems, who have for many years planted it in their cemeteries. I noticed in Algiers that many Moslems visiting their cemetery, especially on a Friday, carried bunches of Narcissus Tazetta and scattered the flowers on the graves, having pulled each bloom away from the main stalk.

Besides Moggridge's, mentioned above, other good figures are:

Coloured: Burbidge and Baker, Pl. 29.

Jordan et Fourreau, *Icones Florae Europae*, t. 183, as discolor, reproduced in Burbidge's Pl. 31, Fig. 2, and Pl. 32, Fig. 7.

Jordan, t. 185, mediterranea. Burbidge, Pl. 32, 6, a rather more starry flower.

Black and White: Coste's *Fl. de France*, iii., p. 380.

Nicholson's *Dictionary*, Fig. 649.

This form will multiply readily in English gardens, but seldom flowers satisfactorily in the open ground, as it starts its growth with the autumnal rains, producing its flower stem in December, and unless it is protected, or in some favoured western garden, the flowers are small and poorly coloured when they attempt to open in January or February. Tazetta in the wild form is included in the R.H.S. omnibus Section XI., but the garden forms and hybrids form Section VIII.

The larger-flowered variety ' Gloriosus ', apparently of garden origin, is an improvement in all ways on the wild plant. It is one of the best for forcing and appears on the market early in the New Year and has the best fragrance of any. There is a dash of lemon mixed with the Jasmine-like sweetness which is as pleasant a combination as the lemon and sugar of a Shrove Tuesday pancake.

Most of the Tazetta varieties are blessed with a

strong scent. In some, however, there is a curious
undertone, apparent if smelt at strongly and for half
a minute, which is not altogether pleasant. In ' Grand
Soleil d'Or' this after-tang is heavy and suggests
leather, and the lemon element is lacking. In ' Grand
Primo Citroniere' and ' Scilly White ' a prolonged
sniff draws out a scent like that of soot.

A garden form listed as ' Mont Cenis ' has a closer
set head of flowers, is dwarf and stiff in stalk and leaf,
and coming in a little later than ' Gloriosus ' is useful
for pot work. A small form sold by nurserymen as
N. canaliculatus flowers later than its near relations
and is a charming dwarf plant for a sheltered nook in
a rock garden. It seems to be the form figured in
Jordan and Fourreau's *Icones* in t. 186 as N. mons-
peliensis, and copied in Burbidge's Pl. 31, Fig. 12.
The true N. canaliculatus of Gussone, according to
Moggridge, is found in the French and Italian Rivieras
and is distinguished by having such narrow perianth
segments that they do not overlap one another but
spread out to form a star-shaped flower. It is not
known to be in cultivation. Closely related small
forms are insolita from Antibes, of Jordan's *Icones*,
t. 184, and Burbidge's Fig. 12 on his Pl. 31, with a
misshapen corona; and the better-formed pratensis,
Jordan, *Icones*, t. 187, and Fig. 5, and Burbidge's
Pl. 32.

N. remopolensis of Panizzi, figured on Pl. 70 of
Bicknell's *Flowering Plants of the Riviera*, somewhat
resembles canaliculatus in its starry perianth and differs
from other orange and white Tazetta forms in the
greater length and narrowness of its corona.

Herbert's corcyrensis of his *Amaryllidaceae*, Pl. 37,
Fig. 1, from Corfu, and Jordan and Fourreau's gany-
medoides, *Icones*, t. 182, from Narbonne, are much
alike—both have reflexing perianth segments and lobed
coronas. A form sent to me from Mount Helicon

resembles the latter but has an entire margin to the corona. It is shown on Pl. XI.

The largest form that has been found apparently wild is N. elatus of Gussone, figured by Bicknell in *Flowering Plants of the Riviera*, Pl. 70, A, who states that it resembles a gigantic N. Tazetta but is distinguishable by its few flowers and wide open crown. It has been found near Naples, Lucca and Taggia and in Olive Gardens near Florence. Most likely with good cultivation the heads would carry more flowers, and then it would be so much like N. Trewianus as to suggest an escape into the wild of that plant, for which no native locality is known. There is a specimen in the British Museum Herbarium from Olive Gardens near Florence, a very suitable locality for the naturalisation of garden escapes.

N. Trewianus, Gawler in *Bot. Mag.*, is an emendation (under t. 1298) of the name ' N. orientalis, Narcissus of the Levant ', accompanying the Fig. 940. This was the largest and handsomest of the polyanthus forms grown by the florists of the seventeenth and eighteenth centuries. Its native country is not known and it was imported from the East, chiefly from Constantinople, wherefore it was one of those named N. orientalis, byzantinus and constantinopolitanus. This last seems to hold the record number of syllables for a specific name.

It is the Mussart his Daffodil of Parkinson's *Paradisus*, the Musarto of Ferrari's *Flora* of 1638, Muzart orientalis of Dutch catalogues and Bazelman major of Haworth's *Monograph*, p. 9. In More's *Flower Garden Display'd* (1734) it is figured in the group for March and called the white Bosleman Narcissus, and it is said to have come from Turkey.

The poet Gray in a letter of March 10th, 1755, mentions that ' the Bozzleman Narcissus blows 9 in. high (3 flowers) and the leaves 25 in. long '. It is beautifully figured by Sydenham Edwards in *Bot. Mag.*, t. 940, showing three flowers, 2 inches across with wide, flat cups, deep yellow shaded with orange. In the description Gawler states that it differs from Tazetta by a crown more manifestly trilobate, more crenulate and patent, blooming earlier than poeticus or biflorus, but later than Tazetta. Sweet's figure, *Brit. Fl. Gard.*, Second Series, ii., t. 118, shows six flowers rather larger than in Edwards's figure. Jordan and Fourreau's *Icones*, t. 188, is another good figure, one flower of which is copied by Burbidge as Fig. 10 on Pl. 31, who also devoted Pl. 30 to the same plant as orientalis. Gawler's statement as to the inter-mediate flowering period, and Burbidge's that 'Tazetta ranges from N. poeticus and N. biflorus (to which some of the N. orientalis and N. Cypri forms figured in the *Botanical Magazine* are very nearly related) to small white-flowered kinds', lead us to assume that these robust, flat-cupped forms are the forerunners of the modern Poetaz varieties which seem likely to oust them from our gardens. It will be a great pity if so beautiful and fairly hardy a plant as N. Trewianus should be lost to cultivation.

Closely related forms with orange cups, most likely of garden origin, are Jordan's t. 190, N. crispicorona of Haworth with a large cup with fluted, deep orange rim; subcrenata Haworth, Bazelman medius of gar-dens; crenulata Haworth, Bazelman minor; flexiliflora Haworth and corrugata Jordan.

N. cypri, as figured by Sweet, Second Series, i., t. 92, is rather more slender than Trewianus with a paler cup, but of much the same general appearance. He and Haworth take it to be the single form of the well-known doubles of their day, one of which is the N. orientalis var. fl. pl. *Bot. Mag.* t. 1011.

These were imported in quantity from Italy as Double Roman Narcissus and varied greatly as to the manner of doubling—Burbidge's Pl. 34 represents the most compact form. They were much used for forcing and growing in glasses in water, but have gone out of favour of late. This may be due to the introduction to England in 1889 of the Chinese variety 'The Grand Emperor', known as 'Water Fairy Flower', 'Sacred Chinese Lily' and 'Good Luck' or 'New Year Lily', so easily grown in water or soil. Immense rough-looking bulbs with many noses and offsets are largely imported from Japan, and some of these will produce from five to ten flower stems. The flowers are white with orange cups very much like those of 'Gloriosus', with an equally delicious fragrance, but they are longer in the tube and have a more symmetrical cup. It varies a little, and the best single-flowered forms are very bold and pleasing in form and texture, although the variety, either by special feeding or natural vigour, is so large in all its members. The leaves can be over a foot in length and an inch wide at flowering time, and the topmost flower another 5 inches above them.

Double-flowered forms are sometimes mixed with the single-flowered bulbs, but are less vigorous, and the doubling is not so regular and pleasing as that of the Double Roman. As Burbidge noticed, the lateral offsets produce their flowers before the central one and bear a greater number.

This suggests that the bulbs have been treated in some way to encourage the production of offsets within the mother-bulb, perhaps by hot-water treatment, which has that effect upon some Daffodils.

So Moku, the well-known illustrated work on Japanese plants, figures the single form in vol. 5, Pl. 53, as N. Tazetta var. chinensis. It is a good black-and-white plate, showing the long tube clearly, but the dissection shows the style shorter than the upper anthers, a deeply six-lobed corona, and a curious thickening at the base of the style that I have never seen in living specimens.

The Useful Plants of Japan (Tokyo, 1895) contains coloured figures of single and double forms. The former is said to grow on sea coasts of warm provinces and to shoot up its peduncle to a height of a foot in Winter. There are several varieties of the double form with narrow leaves, narrow petals or green flowers. All are precious Winter-blooming plants and grow well in water. The bulbs are very poisonous, but in a fresh state are used as medicine. Good figures from photographs appeared in *The Garden*, May 17th and June 21st, 1890, the latter as grown in a garden in Hong-Kong. An excellent one of the double form can be found in *Garden and Forest*, New York, March 21st, 1888.

Both the single and double forms must have been cultivated from very early times in China. The *Studio* extra number for 1928 entitled *Flower and Still-Life Painting* contains a beautiful plate (No. 18) of Narcissus Flowers by Chao Meng-Chien (Sung Dynasty, thirteenth century). It shows seven heads of N. Tazetta, one of which bears single flowers and the others represent the double form.

Personal experience shows that when they are grown in water the best results are obtained from vessels deep enough to allow the roots to descend for at least 4 inches before reaching the bottom. The bulbs can be raised by stones between but not under them, and the water should cover the bulb. They should be grown singly in a deep vase and kept from toppling over by stones lodged at the sides of the bulb. Those grown in pots and soil throve the best in the last trial. Others planted late in the season by the side of a small pool, and some in moist ground, flowered well in the latter part of April.

None of the forms in Series I., Section *b*, have been

found wild; they seem to have been raised in Holland,
perhaps by crossing orange-cupped forms with white.

The oldest and best known is Hermione citrina of
Haworth, which is the N. orientalis γ, Gawler in
Bot. Mag., t. 946, t. 180 of Jordan's *Icones*, and Fig. 6,
Pl. 31, of Burbidge, and the ' Grand Primo Citroniere ' of florists. It is an early-flowering form
with close heads of many flowers, much grown in
Guernsey, Scilly and elsewhere for market, where it
appears early in February and is sold under the
shortened name of ' Primo '. It has a strong Jasmine-
like scent, white perianth and a pale citron cup. The
style is long and carries the stigma out of the throat
to stand above the bases of the upper anthers.

Salisbury identified his H. floribunda with the
' Grand Primo Citroniere ' of the shops, but wrote
that it did not agree with the *Bot. Mag.* Fig. 946.
Haworth places floribunda of Salisbury as the ' Grand
Monarque ' of gardeners. Both Graebner and Baker
refer it to Jordan's t. 181, which Burbidge copied
for his Pl. 31, Fig. 3, and calls 'Grand Monarque '.
It is difficult now to disentangle this confusion, but
it seems most likely that Salisbury's floribunda was
' Grand Monarque ' and that Haworth and the others
named above distinguished the two plants correctly.

The ' Primo ' obtainable in shops varies a good
deal, and there is undoubtedly more than one strain
of it grown for cutting. Also it is used as a catch-
crop in Tomato houses in the Channel Isles, where
for the sake of the following crop it is grown with a
minimum of watering, which somewhat alters the
character of the flower. When growing luxuriantly it
is much finer and nearly as large as ' Grand Monarque '.
It has been grown on grassy slopes of St. Michael's
Mount, Cornwall, for some 150 years, and has been
mentioned in works on British Botany as though it
were an escaped and naturalised plant. The bulbs

were, however, obtained from the Scilly Isles and have increased and grown vigorously, but except in size of flower and height of stem, according to the suitability of situations, they show no variation. It is about ten years since any were replanted; and cut flowers kindly sent to me by Lord St. Levan early in February were the finest in size and number of blooms to the head I have ever seen in citrina.

' Scilly White ' is very much like the last kind, but has a less regular cup and the style only reaches to the bases of the lower anthers. Its stem is not so much furrowed, the head of flowers less compact, the leaves more upright and the whole plant taller than citrina. Nothing definite is known regarding its introduction to the Scilly Isles. It may be the form Salisbury called Hermione leucoifolia, which Haworth named tereticaulis and Gawler N. orientalis a, the pale-cupped white garden Narcissus, in the *Bot. Mag.*, t. 1298. In 1812 Salisbury wrote: ' This will thrive anywhere, and forces admirably, but whether indigenous in the South of Europe or an artificial production of some Dutch florist is yet uncertain.'

A somewhat similar form with a longer style is listed as ' French Monarque '. It is good for gentle forcing to flower in February and has greater substance in the flower than ' White Pearl ' or ' Snowflake ', which have too much of the papyraceous strain in them.

' Grand Monarque ' has the largest and best-formed flowers of the citron-cupped group. It forces well but flowers later than the others. It is evidently, as Haworth and Jordan considered, the floribunda of Salisbury, confused by him with ' Grand Primo Citroniere ' in the *Trans. Hort. Soc.*, 1812. There is a good figure in Jordan's *Icones*, t. 181, and of one flower copied from it in Burbidge's Pl. 31, Fig. 3.

Haworth renamed it ' The Nosegay ' in his *Monograph*, describing the cup as wide, citron, suberect, undivided, and adding: 'The Grand Monarque of gardens of which I have seen many minor Dutch varieties.'

Some of these seedlings raised in Dutch gardens appear occasionally in stocks of other varieties, or can be found under names. One is grown in Scilly as ' Minor Monarque ', with a narrow cup and long, twisting, pointed segments possibly derived from N. italicus. Another called compressa is more like ' Grand Monarque ', but has a reflexing perianth that may not appeal to the florist's eye but gives a certain grace and originality to a very pretty flower. It is not the compressa of Haworth, which is a form of N. intermedius.

The only variety of these citron-cupped Tazettas that I have found satisfactory for growing in the open is ' Grand Monarque '. This is a fine garden plant for a sheltered bed in front of a wall or hedge, and is magnificent as grown on the Riviera and in Algiers, where it forms large clumps and throws up a succession of flowers among stronger and handsomer leaves than it produces in England.

Tazettinae. Series II. albae. (Perianth and corona white.) N. papyraceus, as described by Ker Gawler under t. 947 of the *Botanical Magazine* in 1806, is regarded as the typical form of the group. It is the largest and most vigorous, and is chiefly found in cultivated ground, where it multiplies rapidly by division of the bulbs, which facts suggest a garden origin.

It would have been better if some undoubtedly wild form had been selected as the typical subspecies. Research and experiments might help us to construct a family tree tracing the white-flowered group back to a common ancestor, but with present knowledge it can only be guesswork. A link is missing between

the North African N. pachybolbus and the European
N. dubius of France, N. Panizzianus of Italy or
N. niveus of Spain. Would that the Balearic Isles
might some day yield up such a hidden treasure!

Dealing first with the African forms, *N. Broussonetii* of Lagasca (*Gen. et Spec.*, p. 13) in general
appearance belongs to the white-flowered group of
N. Tazetta, but is so distinct from all other Narcissi
in the extreme rudimentary condition or even entire
absence of the corona, and the protrusion of the anthers,
that Gay considered it as forming a monotypic genus
Aurelia.

The large white flowers with conspicuous yellow
anthers certainly look more like those of a small
Cooperia than a Narcissus, and led F. W. Burbidge
to write: 'It is possible that this plant may be the
result of a cross between a Narcissus and some
other Amaryllidaceous plant belonging to a different
genus.'

It is a native of Mogador on the western coast of
Africa in Long. 30°, and N. canariensis in the Canary
Isles is the only species with a more south-westerly
distribution. It may represent a stage in the development of plants with coronas as found in Narcissus,
from those with Crinum-shaped flowers.

It is of course tender, coming from so southern
a locality, and has seldom been cultivated successfully in England. It flowered at Kew and elsewhere
in 1887. Good figures are to be found in the *Bot.
Mag.*, t. 7016, and in *The Garden*, vol. xxx., June 30th,
1888, drawn from living plants; and Burbidge's Pl. 47
(1875) representing dried specimens.

N. pachybolbus, described by Durieu in Duchartre's
Rev., vol. ii., p. 425, 1846, is a native of Oran in North
Africa. In flower and leaf it closely resembles certain
European Tazetta forms with small flowers, but has
an extraordinarily large bulb $2\frac{1}{2}$ inches in diameter

and 4 in height and a strongly ribbed, flattened scape quite out of proportion with its small flowers.

The leaves are glaucous and except in their greater width resemble those of N. dubius. The flowers of both are similar in size and in the pleasing, rounded outlines of cup and segments. On the slender scape of dubius they are more charming than in the crowded head of twelve to seventeen on the thick scape of the African plant. Good figures of N. pachybolbus are those in the *Bot. Mag.*, t. 6825 (1885), and Burbidge's Pl. 39.

N. canariensis of Herbert, figured in Burbidge's Pl. 48, is the smallest flowered white species known. The flowers are only ½ inch in diameter, but have such long tubes that the heads have but little beauty. It is interesting as extending the range of the genus so far to the south-west, occurring only in the Canaries.

N. dubius of Gouan has flowers almost as small as those of N. pachybolbus, but with the perfect proportions of a well-formed Leedsii, as though seen through the wrong end of a telescope. The whole plant is small and refined with very glaucous, narrow leaves. It is only found in rocky, calcareous ground, amongst Cistus, Helichrysum Staechas and other plants of sunbaked situations, near Toulon, Hyères, Avignon and Montpellier. Moggridge adds Corsica, Barcelona and Greece. This last locality is certainly incorrect, as Halacsy points out in his *Conspectus Florae Graecae*, and the others are rather incredible.

I have not found this charming little plant easy to establish in the open ground. It increases and flowers well in an unheated frame used for species of Crocus, where the lights are closed from June onwards that the soil may become bone dry. This treatment comes nearest to the thorough drying and ripening that dubius must undergo on the rocky ledges where it grows naturally. However, seeds sown in the open ground germinate readily and if undisturbed grow satisfactorily into flowering bulbs, but seldom flower again if planted out on sunny ledges of the rock garden.

The flowers, sometimes described as cream colour or nearly white, in those I grow are pure white when fully open. The cup varies from being slightly lobed to entire, but is always symmetrically formed and nearly hemispherical in outline.

Redouté's Pl. 409 in *Les Liliacées* represents this plant, but is named N. pumilus. Moggridge's figure, Pl. 71 C, is the best. Burbidge's Pl. 27 was drawn from dried specimens and other figures. Abbé Coste's, 3555 in *Fl. de France*, is a good outline. Worthington Smith's in *Gard. Chron.*, xli., p. 246 (1907), makes the cup appear too flat.

Jordan's H. micrantha, as figured t. 176 of his *Icones* and reproduced in Burbidge's Pl. 31, Fig. 8, has even smaller flowers, but may be a form of N. dubius, being only found in the same restricted area near Toulon.

N. Pujolii, described by Font Quer, is a hybrid between dubius and juncifolius.

N. Panizzianus of Parlatore's *Flora Italica* is only known to grow near San Remo. It is figured by Moggridge on his Pl. 71 A, and by Burbidge, Pl. 36, as a slender form with larger, pure white flowers with pointed segments and entire cups. It seems very similar to Loiseleur's N. niveus, and Jordan's Pl. 177 named H. virginea, copied by Burbidge on Pl. 31, Fig. 4, with a three-cleft corona. It was only known to Jordan from cultivated plants. I have lately seen a similar form collected in Asia Minor among Tulips.

Southern Spain seems to be the headquarters of a race varying in size, number of flowers, form and colour of corona, and rounded or pointed segments. It is certainly native there and the crown of the Rock of Gibraltar is whitened in mid-Winter by myriads of its flowers. It occurs also near Malaga; and in Portugal near Lisbon and in Algarve. Its extremes of variation have received separate names. In its pure white, slender form Loiseleur described it as *N. niveus*, and the larger form found in richer soils he named *N. polyanthos*.

According to Willkomm and Lange in *Prodromus Florae Hispanicae*, the latter has shorter leaves, a greater number of flowers with pale yellowish undivided corona. These two forms grown from seed under cultivation may have been the parents of the larger garden varieties.

Jordan's Pl. 178, reproduced by Burbidge, Pl. 31, Fig. 7, represents a specimen from Nice which he considered Loiseleur's polyanthos. It has a flat cup and wide segments very similar to the plant grown for market as 'White Pearl'. Thus N. polyanthos of the lower ground may be a link between Gibraltar's Rock and Covent Garden.

Moggridge's N. papyraceus var. β incurvatus, described in his *Flora of Mentone* and illustrated by an outline figure, is hardly separable from niveus. It may be a trifle larger, but not more so than would be likely if bulbs from Gibraltar were naturalised in cultivated ground, where many of these Tazetta forms establish themselves and grow with increased vigour. It grew near Mentone in the Turin Valley, and flowered later than the larger plant. I believe it to be the form sold in London in the end of February as 'Paper White' when the larger, star-flowered form no longer comes in from France; and that it occurs in Scilly as a rogue among stocks obtained from the Continent.

The last of the group is the largest-flowered form described in the *Botanical Magazine* under Sydenham

Edwards's excellent drawing, t. 947. It is an old
garden plant which has been largely cultivated in
Italy for centuries; and at the present time is grown
in Southern France and Egypt, and exported in vast
quantities as bulbs for forcing and as cut flowers.
It forces so easily that it can be brought into flower
in December and is always the first Narcissus to
appear in the markets, providing a welcome suggestion of Spring and a change from the Chrysanthemums
that have reigned supreme for the last three months.
The earliest bunches come chiefly from the South of
France, and a succession is maintained well into March
from Guernsey and Scilly. It is known as N. papyraceus grandiflorus, or major, 'The Paper White'.

It has a starry outline, as the perianth segments are
longer as compared with the cup than in all other
Tazetta forms except italicus and chrysanthus, which
are possibly garden forms derived from it. The
perianth and segments are pure white, slightly transparent and flimsy in substance when compared with
the opaque, firm texture found in all the Tazettas with
yellow cups.

'Paper White' has also a somewhat over-sweet scent
that some consider sickly, as it lacks the refreshing,
sharp blend of citron to be found in 'Gloriosus',
'Double Roman' and other forms.

It is abundant, apparently as a naturalised plant,
in cultivated ground from the Basses Pyrénées, Portugal and Spain, through the French Riviera into
Italy, frequently interspersed with some of the small
and local forms already described. Unfortunately
they are all too tender to flourish in an average English
garden, chiefly owing to their habit of appearing above
ground soon after they have been watered by the
first autumnal rains, as is the rule with so many African
and Mediterranean bulbous plants.

There are other good figures in Moggridge, *Fl.*

of Mentone, Pl. 70; Bicknell, *Plants of the Riviera*, 69 A; Burbidge, *Narcissus*, Pl. 35; and Coste, *Fl. de France*, 3554 in outline

Tazettinae. Series III. luteae. N. *italicus* was first described and named by Gawler in the *Botanical Magazine* for 1809 with a very good figure, t. 1188. Haworth made four species, two from Tenore's praecox and Loiseleur's subalbidus, but Hermione straminea and tenuiflora he invented himself. They are based on such slight variant characters that they are not worth consideration even as varieties.

The perianth is generally described as ' pale brimstone ', ' yellowish white ', ' nearly white ' and so forth. The last is the best description, as many a Narcissus generally accepted as ' white ' is no purer than the fully expanded blossoms of italicus. The suggestion of yellow in the perianth and its lemon-yellow corona have led to its inclusion in the group Tazettinae luteae, and it makes a connecting link between the white N. papyraceus and the yellow N. chrysanthus, as all three have similarly starry perianths and narrow cups. N. italicus has been known to sow itself freely in gardens on the French Riviera and to reproduce itself true to type, so that even if it had a hybrid origin it is now a fixed form.

Gawler described the style as advanced beyond the anthers to the level of the crown, whereas in papyraceus it does not surpass the anthers. A long style is found in most of the other luteae forms, but is very short in chrysanthus, which Herbert and Coste considered a colour variety of italicus. It may be that both have arisen from the crossing of papyraceus with some yellow form.

Gawler only knew italicus as a form imported annually from Italy together with papyraceus, ' Double Roman ' and a large yellow-flowered form, the H. multiflora of Haworth's *Monograph*, and therefore as a cultivated plant. Perhaps it was this customary association that induced Herbert to look upon the two 'Double Roman' forms known to him as 'cultivated varieties of italicus'. Bicknell in *Flowering Plants of the Riviera* calls it a native of Nice, Pegli, Siena, Naples and Capri; Coste records it only in 'bords des champs' in France.

It may be the N. sulphureis coloris majusculus of Clusius in the *Curae posteriores*, p. 62, and Parkinson's N. sulphureus major, p. 70 of the *Paradisus*. Bicknell's Pl. 69 B in *Flowering Plants of the Riviera* is good, drawn from a six-flowered specimen. Coste's *Fl. de France*, Fig. 3553, represents it in outline.

It is a strong grower, but in the average English garden flowers too late and too sparsely to be worth growing. In favoured localities near the sea it has succeeded better, though the flowers are smaller than those of Southern France, where they measure 2 inches across the starry perianth and are produced freely from January to March. After the hot summer of 1933 clumps that had not flowered for several seasons bore many heads in April, 1934.

Besides N. italicus, Baker made his Series III. to include three other subspecies, Bertolonii of Jordan, aureus of Loiseleur, and cupularis of Salisbury, grouping a number of allied forms, possibly of garden origin, under the last two.

N. Bertolonii is described as a species by Parlatore in the *Flora Italica* and by Jordan, who in t. 192 of his *Icones* represents a specimen from Pisa, rather paler in colour than the excellent Fig. B of Pl. 90 in Moggridge's *Flora of Mentone*, drawn from a cultivated plant originally obtained from terraces at San Remo. Parlatore had only found it near Lucca and at Pisa. Though rare in Europe, it is more abundant in North Africa, where I collected it from ploughed land and saw it growing on steep, rocky hillsides near Algiers and Chiffa.

I regard it as a wild species and possibly the parent
of the numerous garden forms with yellow perianths.

It may be the plant sent to Clusius by Dr. Simon
de Tovar of Seville, which is the fifth of the wide-leaved
forms on p. 156 of the *Historia* having yellow flowers
with orange cups. The woodcut used for this is a
good representation of Bertolonii. It was used by Lobel
ten years earlier for one with a white perianth (and quite
wrongly in Johnson's Gerard for the Primrose peerlesse,
N. biflorus), but most of these old writers used any
block that was to hand and not too much unlike the
plant they were describing. Parkinson's N. Africanus
aureus minor, the lesser Barbary Daffodil with a poor
figure, No. 2 on p. 81, seems intended for N. Bertolonii.

The plant from Algiers thrives best planted out in an
unheated frame, and increases freely by offsets. The
bulbs have a remarkably smooth, rich brown tunic, which
corresponds with Clusius's description ' externo cortice
spadicei[1] coloris praeditus '. It has also settled down
and flowers freely on sunny ledges of the rock garden.

In his *Amaryllideae* Baker separated N. aureus of
Loiseleur from H. cupularis of Salisbury. His descriptions differ chiefly as to the colour of the corona,
' orange yellow ' for cupularis and ' a little darker than
the segments ' for aureus; in both of these subspecies, as
he termed them, he described the perianth as ' lemon
yellow '. He cites many of Haworth and Jordan's
so-called species as allied to one or other according to
the depth of their colouring.

I believe the twenty-three names thus arranged
belong to cultivated forms, a few of which have escaped
and become naturalised in Southern France and Italy.
Thus of eleven yellow-flowered Tazetta forms described
by Jordan in *Breviarum plantarum novarum*, nine are
said to be cultivated specimens whose native country is

[1] Spadiceus was used for a date-brown and also of a bay horse.

unknown. The remaining two were found round Grasse, where so many strays from cultivation occur.

It seems to me possible that the yellow-flowered Tazettas could have been raised in gardens from a wild parent such as Bertolonii, those of paler colouring having a bicolor form as one parent. They can be arranged in a chain with very slight differences between its links from Jordan's chlorotica (t. 191 of his *Icones*, copied in Burbidge's Fig. 11, Pl. 31) with sulphur perianth and a yellow cup, through the *Bot. Mag.*, t. 1026, as N. orientalis δ, which is H. multiflora of Haworth's *Monograph*, with perianth of a pale buffish yellow and light orange cup. Nearer the other end of the series is Haworth's H. aperticorona of Sweet's *Brit. Fl. Gard.*, Second Series, vol. ii., t. 191, a rich yellow flower with a saucer-shaped, orange cup very little smaller or less brilliant than the deepest in colour, the well-known ' Soleil d'Or '. Aperti-corona may be the Rhyvan Narcissus of Furber's plate for March. These fine plates, issued in 1730, were drawn by Peter Casteels to illustrate groups of flowers produced in each of the twelve months. Two years later they were re-engraved to illustrate the quarto called *The Flower-garden Displayed*, the text of which is attributed to Sir Thomas More in Martyn's Edition of Miller's *Gardeners' Dictionary*. The Rhyvan Narcissus is there said to have been raised in Holland and lately sent to England, having blossoms like that which is called ' Soleil d'Or ', yellow with cups of an orange colour.

Until the arrival of the gorgeous ' Fortune ', ' Soleil d'Or ' was one of the most brilliant yellow forms with cups of an orange that nearly approaches scarlet, and is still one of the best of the Tazettas for vigour, size, earliness and scent, as well as for colour. Its vigour under cultivation suggests a garden origin, possibly in North Africa, from the native N. Bertolonii.

The N. luteus Aphricus from Argieria and Char-
tagina of Lobel's *Adversaria,* 1571, or the N. africanus
flavus polyanthes of the *Additamenta ad curas posteriores*
of Clusius, sent to Christian Porretus from France
under the name of Narcisse d'Algier, which flowered in
1611, might be N. Bertolonii or the larger plant. Parkinson's figure on p. 81 certainly represents the latter.
He called it ' N. africanus aureus major, Narcisse
d'Algiers, or, as in the Low Countries, Narcissen van
Heck, in English the Great Barbary Daffodil '. It is
one of the best of his drawings, of the actual size of
a well-grown "Soleil d'Or ' of the present day.

As stated above, the name ' Soleil d'Or ' was used
for a plant well known in English gardens in 1732,
but its first conjunction with a binomial Latin name
occurs in 1812, when Salisbury in vol. i., *Trans. Hort.
Soc.*, used the name Hermione cupularis, unaccom-
panied by any sufficient description, but intending it
to cover the figures he cites, viz. t. 925, *Bot. Mag.*, and
Redouté's t. 17 in *Les Liliacées* (1802). The latter is
a beautiful drawing of an eight-flowered head, described
by A. P. De Candolle, who wrote the text for the first
four volumes. He follows Linnæus and treats all
the wide-leaved, many-flowered Narcissi as Tazetta;
but adds ' when the flowers are entirely yellow it
generally bears the name of Narcisse de Constantinople '.

Sydenham Edwards's t. 925 of the *Bot. Mag.*,
vol. 24, for 1806 is also named simply N. Tazetta. It
is brilliantly coloured and the best portrait of the plant.
Gawler in the text only differentiates this yellow form
by citing the africanus aureus of Parkinson and Bauhin.
Both of these plates certainly represent the same plant
(Gawler cites Redouté's), and Salisbury terms them
' Sol D'or, Floristis Batavis '.

An even earlier figure is referred to in *Les Liliacées.*
It occurs as N. 3 in Knorr's *Thesaurus* or *Regnum*

Florae, published in 1772, is rather stiff in the drawing but well and richly coloured, and among its names is ' The yellow Daffodil with much flowers '.

Haworth in 1831 retained the name cupularis for Salisbury's plant, citing the figures in *Les Liliacées* and the *Botanical Magazine*, and he calls it the ' Soleil d'Or Hortulanorum '.   Herbert repeated this in 1837. Loiseleur in 1827 described N. aureus in *Nouvelle notice sur les plantes à ajouter à la Flore de France*. He gives a good coloured figure as N. aureus in his *Herbier Générale des Amateurs* in t. 147.   This is correctly coloured for the garden plant, and he gives the name as ' Grand Soleil d'Or ' and cites Redouté's plate and t. 925 of the *Botanical Magazine*, but confuses matters by also citing *Bot. Mag.*, t. 1026, the paler form which is Haworth's H. multiflora.

Moggridge's excellent figure, Pl. 22, in his *Contribution to the Flora of Mentone* of 1874, is paler in colouring as compared with that of the *Bot. Mag.*, t. 925, but the colouring of many plates in this work is paler than in the living flowers.

Moggridge wrote: ' N. aureus Lois. is, I believe, the Soleil d'Or of our gardens, and perhaps may owe much of its beauty to the effects of cultivation.

' It has long been considered as one of the wild species . . . though always ranked among the more doubtful natives.'

Jordan's H. aurea, t. 194, represents a still paler specimen, and he cites Haworth's multiflora in connection with it.   Now Haworth meant this to cover N. orientalis δ (*Bot. Mag.*, t. 1026), which is a close-headed florists' variety ' usually imported by the seedsmen from Italy along with Double Roman, Paper White or Italian kinds '.

From these confusing pieces of evidence we may conclude that ' Soleil d'Or ' is an old plant of unknown origin; but very early in its history regarded as from an African source. As it is not known as a wild plant in North Africa, but its smaller counterpart N. Bertolonii is plentiful there, it may have been raised from the latter in some garden. It bore the French name of ' Soleil d'Or '; and although De Candolle does not mention this name in *Les Liliacées* in 1802, it was well known by it in English gardens as early as 1732, and Salisbury in 1812, under his cupularis, calls it the Soleil d'Or of Dutch florists.

Therefore, seeing that these large yellow-flowered forms are almost certainly of garden origin, they do not deserve latinised specific names, but if one must be used for the group cupularis should be chosen as being the oldest.

XVI

Tazetta Hybrids

Intermediates between N. Tazetta and poeticus fall
into four classes: spontaneous crosses, such as biflorus
and some allied forms; presumed crosses, of which
Bazelman major, Cypri, etc., of Oriental origin are
examples; the recorded crosses of recent years, such
as those of Messrs. Van der Schoot raised in Holland;
and still later races with a better form of poeticus as
one parent mostly raised in Cornwall by Mr. P. D.
Williams.

N. biflorus owes its name to W. Curtis, who described
it under t. 197 of the *Botanical Magazine* in 1792.
It was a common garden plant in England in the
sixteenth century according to Gerard. He calls it
the Common white Daffodil or Primrose peerlesse,
N. medioluteus, but the figure he uses for it is that
used by Tabernaemontanus for his N. medioluteus I.,
a five-flowered Tazetta form, and his II. is also a
Tazetta with seven flowers, used again by Gerard for
his N. pisanus. Johnson in his edition of Gerard
uses a block which is Clusius's N. latifolius flore
prorsus flavo, showing three flowers, which may be
N. Bertolonii, and is also used by Lobel for N. albidus
medioluteus. These three figures are not in any way
like the biflorus of Curtis, and are good warnings as
to how much reliance to place on illustrations used by
these old writers.

Parkinson's Fig. 1 on p. 75, though crude, is a good
representation of the true plant. He describes it as
one-flowered but most commonly two, adding ' seldom
three or more ', possibly out of deference to the illus-

trations used by earlier writers. It would be difficult to improve upon his further observation that it is 'Whitish cream colour somewhat . . . of a pale Primrose . . . with a small round flat crowne rather than a cup, being of a sweete but stuffing scent. The root is reasonable great and encreasing more than a better plant.'

It seems to be the plant Clusius refers to in the *Historia* as spontaneous in England. Parkinson could never hear of its natural place of growth here. Ray saw it in fields near Hornsey Church, and quoted Mr. Sherard's evidence in the *Synopsis methodica stirpium Britanicarum* (1724).

I remember it in some meadows near Paignton sixty years ago, and it has been recorded from several English counties and near Dublin, but it can only be a naturalised alien in these localities. It seems to have occurred spontaneously near Montpellier in France.

Where N. Tazetta and poeticus grow together, forms more closely resembling Tazetta, and having a greater number of flowers in the head, were recorded by Grenier and Godron as N. Tazetto-poeticus. This is the N. medio-luteus of Miller's *Gardeners' Dictionary*, N. cothurnalis of Salisbury. A cothurnus was a high boot or buskin worn by tragic actors. The long, loose spathe of this plant reaching above the ovary suggested the name.

Salisbury regarded it as 'One of Nature's mules', having carefully dissected more than a thousand specimens without finding even the rudiment of a seed, though they bore perfect pollen. Burbidge, on the contrary, declares that the anthers seldom develop perfect pollen and its ovules are often abortive, but if fertilised with pollen from another species it can bear seed.

It is figured by Sowerby in *English Botany*, t. 276;

in Redouté's *Les Liliacées*, t. 405, it is rather too white and has a slight touch of red on the edge of the crown, perhaps an exaggeration in the retouching by hand of these colour-printed plates. Reichenbach, *Fl. Germ.*, ix., t. 365, Burbidge, t. 41, Coste, *Fl. de France*, Fig. 3557, are other figures.

The second class contains plants that suggest the crossing of a Tazetta with poeticus, but of which no definite evidence is available.

Sweet's figure of Hermione Cypri, *Brit. Fl. Gard.*, Series II., vol. i., t. 92, and H. Trewiana, Series II., vol. ii., t. 118, of the same work, are examples of these plants which were mostly imported from Constantinople, and variously named orientalis, Bazelman major and grandiflorus. They have been dealt with among the Tazettinae bicolores, which they resemble so closely, see pp. 155 and 156.

The present-day race classed as Poetaz varieties owes its origin to the Dutch firm of Messrs. R. Van der Schoot. In the year 1885 large stocks of Tazetta varieties were growing in their Nursery at Hillegom alongside beds of N. poeticus ornatus, and the experiment of crossing these was decided upon.

N. poeticus was used as the seed parent and some of the best yellow Tazettas and such bicolors as ' Grand Monarque ', ' Gloriosus ' and Bazelman major were chosen for pollen. A good crop of seed was produced, and early in the present century selected varieties had been grown into large stocks and were brought before the public.

They differ from the older, Oriental varieties in showing more of the poeticus characters, having larger perianths, flatter cups and fewer flowers in the head, usually from four to eight.

Many of them are still among the most useful kinds of bunch-flowered Narcissi for growing in pots to be forced gently to follow the true Tazettas. They fall into two groups, those with white and those with yellow perianths.

White forms are 'Alsace', which shows much poeticus influence in shape and a slight red edge to the cup in young flowers; 'Aspasia', which bears four to five flowers, and 'Elvira', one of the best for forcing and open air. Some years ago a fine double variety of 'Elvira' appeared in Messrs. Van der Schoot's stock and is the widely known 'Cheerfulness', so good for all purposes; a strong grower and lasting long as a cut flower, coming into flower rather late in the garden and good for pot work if not forced. It well deserves the award received in the Wisley Trials in 1927.

'Ideal', 'Irma', 'Triumph' and 'Early Perfection' come from the same firm. 'Laurens Koster', raised by the late Albert Vis, 'Innocence' and 'Orange Blossom' are also good varieties with white perianths and orange cups.

By using a better form of poeticus as one parent still larger forms have been raised, especially in Cornwall. 'St. Agnes', raised by Mr. P. D. Williams, is so far the finest as a garden plant. It received its first award in 1926 as a show flower and another later, as a garden plant, after trial at Wisley. It has a well-formed, white perianth and rich orange cup, and lasts long in good condition in the open.

'Glorious', raised by Mr. J. C. Williams, received the F.C.C. in 1926. It has a widely expanded cup of orange scarlet and a perianth almost as ample and flat as some of the best poeticus forms. It is figured on p. 178 of Mr. Calvert's *Daffodil Growing*.

'Medusa's' cup is smaller but almost as brilliant in colour. It generally has two flowers to the head, comes into bloom early and is very successful as a market and garden variety, increasing fast and flowering freely. Figured in *Gard. Chron.*, March 20th, 1920,

Calvert, p. 179. 'Kingcraft' has a smaller flower with beautifully rounded perianth, Calvert, p. 181. 'Geranium' of Van der Schoot has the largest flowers of any.

Several of the Dutch-raised varieties with a yellow perianth are widely grown and excellent for pots. 'Jaune à Merveille' is the largest and carries eight flowers. 'Klondyke', 'Irene' and 'Admiration' are others of Van der Schoot's raising. The last is pale yellow with a red-rimmed cup, and resembles a Barrii in appearance. It is especially good in the gardens of the French Riviera.

'Orange Cup' (Tromp Brothers) and 'Canary Bird' are good yellow forms. Two Cornish varieties, 'Scarlet Gem' and 'Halvose', have yellow perianths of good substance, and the fiery orange of the cup runs out along the margin of the segments, producing a cheerful simulation of reflected firelights. Both are excellent for forcing under glass, but grow freely in the open and pay handsomely in richer colouring for a position sheltered from cutting winds. They were raised by Mr. P. D. Williams.

'Silver Chimes', raised by Mr. Martin in Cornwall, is the most exquisitely refined of all polyanthus forms, both in delicacy of colouring and the charm of its poise and proportions. It is classed as 5b, that is a triandrus hybrid, but in general appearance, vigour of growth, width of leaf and number of flowers it resembles its other parent.

The flowers average six to eight in the bunch; the first to open stand upright, while younger blooms and buds are pendent like those of their triandrus parent. The perianth measures about 2 inches across and is white, with a crystalline shimmer and smoothness of texture inherited from triandrus. The corona is longer than in Tazetta, being two-thirds of an oval in outline, and pale citron yellow.

XVII

POETICUS

THE FIRST use of the name poeticus was by Lobel, as
N. poeticus mediocroceus purpureus, in *Stirpium Adversaria Nova* in 1570. Tabernaemontanus also used it
in his *Kreuterbuch* in 1588. Linnæus gave it botanical
authority by using it in *Species Plantarum*, defining
it as, spathe one-flowered, limb of corona rotate very
short. In the Second Edition he added scariose
and crenulate.[1] The character of one flower to a
spathe he also applied to Pseudo-Narcissus, Bulbocodium and serotinus, to distinguish them from
Jonquilla and Tazetta, with heads of many flowers.

He made the shape of the corona the distinguishing
character in the four species with one-flowered scapes.
In poeticus it must be rotate, that is wheel-shaped,
circular and flat, in contrast with campanulate, bell-
shaped, in Pseudo-Narcissus; turbinate, cone-shaped,
in Bulbocodium; and very short and six-cleft in serotinus.

It is not clear whether Linnæus knew that the corona
varied in its degree of flatness in certain forms of
poeticus. Mr. Pugsley, after careful examination,
believes that the specimen in the Linnean herbarium
had in life a cup-shaped corona and therefore does
not agree with Linnæus's definition ' rotate ', and he
thinks some form with a cup-shaped corona must be
considered as the type.

This depends on what we consider was in Linnæus's
mind when he used the term rotate. In the *Philo-*

[1] Narcissus spatha uniflora, nectarii limbo rotato brevissimo—
scarioso crenulato.

sophia, published in 1770, he explained the terms he used in botanical descriptions. On p. 52 he defines rotatus as planus, nulli tubo impositus, and Hypocrateriformis as planus, tubo impositus, and for an example of this he refers to his Fig. 142, which is apparently the flower of a Cowslip, judging by the round spots at the throat. Fig. 145 on the same page represents 'Nectarium campanulatum in Narcisso' and consists of a perianth and corona proportioned as in Jonquilla or Tazetta, that is with a shallow cup. Thus it seems probable that any cup less shallow than in these would be regarded by Linnæus as rotate, and that he used it in a wide sense to include slightly concave corollas. Further evidence is found in *Species Plantarum*, where he distinguishes the Oxlip, Primula elatior, by its *plane* flower from the Cowslip with a *concave* flower. Oxlip flowers, however, are not perfectly flat, but slightly concave, though generally described in Latin as 'planus'. Linnæus may have been contented, as in the case of his N. minor, that a variable species should be represented in his Herbarium by a specimen showing some degree of variation from his description.

The corona of N. poeticus dries badly, shrinking and appearing much flatter when dry than when fresh. The two flowers in the Linnean herbarium are no exception, and the best that Mr. Pugsley can say of their coronas is that they are 'apparently cup-shaped' and 'though its precise characters may be indeterminable the specimen certainly recalls the N. patellaris of Salisbury and the plant figured in *English Botany*'.

It seems to be as impossible to recognise a living representative of the Linnean specimen as to discover the identity of the Man in the Iron Mask.

Those who wish to go deeply into the botanical history of N. poeticus should study Mr. H. W. Pugsley's

exhaustive paper, 'Narcissus poeticus and its Allies',
in the *Journal of Botany*, 1915.

He considers there are nine species, and arranges
these in two series, of which the following is an abridged
summary:

I. *Poetici*. Stamens unequal, perianth segments usually shortly
narrowed and imbricate below.

  * Corona flat:

    1. N. poeticus

  ** Corona more or less cupular:

    2. verbanensis, dwarf and small-flowered

    3. hellenicus, plant tall

    4. recurvus, The Pheasant's Eye, large-flowered

    5. majalis, corona with a white zone below red margin.

II. *Radiiflori*. Stamens subequal, perianth segments usually
narrowed below.

  * Corona small, cupular:

    6. radiiflorus, corona $2\frac{1}{2}$ mm. deep, 8 broad

    7. stellaris, corona 2 mm. deep, 10 broad

  ** Corona flat or nearly so when mature:

    8. poetarum, corona wholly red

    9. exertus, corona flat and discoid.

This arrangement is also justified by slight variations
in the shape of the fruits.

For garden purposes, wild or reputedly wild forms
can be distinguished as *early flowering*, of which
ornatus (Pugsley's N. exertus var. β, ornatus) is the
most familiar garden plant, and *late*, as recurvus, the
Pheasant's Eye. Or again by the form of the perianth
segments, whether overlapping to form round flowers
or with narrowed claws resulting in starry flowers.
These last are interesting for botanical collections rather
than for garden value.

As a wild plant *poeticus* has a wide range in montane

pastures in France, Spain, Italy, Switzerland, Austria, Dalmatia and the Balkans, reaching as far as Montenegro and Greece; it is subspontaneous in England, Scandinavia, Denmark, Germany and Belgium; and it is not surprising that it should be so variable. It is generally so abundant where it occurs that miles of mountain-sides are whitened by the masses of its blossoms. I have met with it in the Pyrenees, Le Lautaret and Lanslebourg, and found the colonies very variable, especially at Le Lautaret, where some flowers were starry as a windmill and many so well formed that had they appeared in a seed bed they would be worth naming. Someone leaving that neighbourhood on the Sunday before a R.H.S. Show in early July might easily select a dozen distinct forms of newly opened blooms and stage them for the show on the Tuesday.

It is likely that the old forms known as garden plants to Gerard, Parkinson, Salisbury and Haworth were clones and the vegetative increase of distinct variations selected among colonies of wild ones. The chance of repeating such selections is clearly shown by a photograph reproduced in *The Garden* for March 12th, 1904, in which starry flowers can be seen among others with widely overlapping perianth segments.

Herbert's var. *verbanensis* is a microform found in Italy, Savoy and the Mont Cenis country, but is frail and uncertain in gardens.

Salisbury's *radiiflorus* has a more eastern range; according to M. Correvon it is the prevailing form in the pastures of Château d'Œx above Aigle in the Canton of Vaud. It is well shown in a photograph in *The Garden* for January 2nd, 1904. Curtis's figure, t. 193 in the *Botanical Magazine*, as N. angustifolius, and Fig. 3 in the frontispiece of Pugsley's paper, represent it.

Poeticus ornatus of gardens is a newcomer. It ap-

peared as a cut flower sent to Covent Garden from
Paris; Mr. James Walker went to Paris, learnt where
it was grown and introduced it to England. It is not
the N. ornatus of Haworth, so really has no right to
the name it bears.

Its early-flowering habit makes it easy to force, and
it is a free grower in beds or grass in the open. Though
now outclassed in form, its rounded perianth segments
and brightly ringed cup are not to be despised in their
early season.

Mr. Pugsley makes it a variety of exertus, a name
used by Haworth in his *Revisio* in 1819 for a variety
of his majalis. Its principal feature is found in the
anthers, all six of which are prominent in the throat
of the corona. It may be the form represented by
Redouté's drawing of N. poeticus, t. 160, in vol. iii. of
Les Liliacées.

N. *hellenicus* is a new specific name bestowed by
Mr. Pugsley on the plant known for many years as
N. poeticus verus of Linnæus. He recognises it as
the form represented by herbarium specimens at Kew
and the British Museum, collected by Haussknecht in
Greece.

It is so distinct in its great height and comparatively
small but beautifully rounded flowers that it looks
like a form from an outlying locality far away from the
main distribution. It flowers late and the charm of
its form tends to disappear after the first day, as the
perianth reflexes more than is desirable. Some hybrid
varieties raised from it have had signal successes as
show flowers. ' Crimson Braid ' and ' Dinkie ' owe
their charm to it.

The variety *poetarum* has contributed greatly to
the beauty and history of present-day ' red cups ', as
it has been the source of all their intense colour. It
has a poor perianth, very gappy between the segments,
and its value is centred in its early flowering and a

corona stained throughout with deep red.   It has never
been traced to a wild source, and it is equally ridiculous
to select it as the Narcissus of Ovid and other
poets as to call it ' Saffron-cupped ' as Haworth has
done.

This useful flower has been treated ungratefully
by gardeners after they had got what they wanted
from it, for it has almost disappeared from gardens and
there is no good portrait of it.

N. poeticus recurvus, the Pheasant's Eye, or Sweet
Nancy of some, like the last is not known as a wild
plant.   It is so robust, late-flowering and beautiful that
if its discoverer were known, whether he found it
wild on a hillside or in his seed beds, he would deserve
a monument in Kew Gardens.   Recurvus is figured
by Sweet in *Brit. Fl. Gard.*, Series II., t. 188.   With
the sparkling whiteness of its solid, reflexing segments
and the brilliant colouring of its greenish-yellow cup
ringed with crimson it comes as a grand finale to the
end of the Daffodil season.

Its scent is almost too powerful if many blooms are
brought into any but a very large room.   There is a
great deal of nutmeg odour about it that is delightful
in the open air, but on a dinner table is disastrous
to the palate, causing all delicate flavours to partake
of nutmeg.   A similar result, but with a different
type of savour, comes from bunches of Almond,
Azalea mollis or Sweet Peas when too close to dinner
plate and wineglass.

A form with a spathe unlike that of any other
Narcissus is the latest addition to the wild forms of
poeticus.   It is described by M. Beauverd in *Bull.
Soc. Bot. Genève*, Series II., xxiii., p. 549 (1931), as
N. poeticus var. physaloides.   The exaggerated in-
flation of the spathe causes it to resemble the enlarged
calyx of Physalis, the Winter Cherry, and suggested
the name.   After the flower has emerged the spathe

remains dilated below and bears two tongue-shaped lobes at its summit.

Garden-raised varieties of N. poeticus are so numerous that it has become a hard task to provide fresh names of poets or styles of poetry for the new-comers.

Mr. Engleheart has enriched gardens with many lovely flowers with charming names. His 'Horace' was one of the first, and I have heard him say that he would not have believed a prophet who told him that the small bed of this variety, which at one time contained the whole stock, would in so short a time have provided the old and new worlds with millions of bulbs of this popular flower. Its parents were ornatus and poetarum, and it inherited good features from both, especially earliness, a wide perianth and a brilliantly edged cup.

These garden varieties can be roughly divided into two sets, those with the corona yellow, edged with a narrow red ring, and those with the corona suffused with orange, deepening towards the edge to vermilion or crimson. There are, however, many intermediate forms.

The red-ringed varieties are the most numerous, and some of the most distinct were raised by Mr. Engleheart. Among his best are 'Huon', 'Wide Wing', 'Papyrus', 'Opera' and 'Laureate', and also the two, 'Sea Green' and 'Much Afraid', illus-trated on the plate facing page 184. Both of these have remarkably flat cups with such distinct crimson rings that they produce a wide-eyed, startled expression in the flower.

'Snow King' (Dawson) is a good early form, very useful for cutting over a long period if some are grown at the foot of a south wall and others in open posi-tions.

'Sarchedon' and 'Sonata', two Engleheart seedlings, have very large perianth segments. The first is excellent for forcing and a good, all-round garden plant.

' Marseillaise ' (Chapman) is a small, round, very bright flower, its flat orange cup neatly edged with crimson. ' Dactyl ' and ' Hexameter ' are other beautiful varieties well named. Others as good, but lacking the titular connection with poetry, are ' Raeburn ', ' Ringdove ', ' Dulcimer ', ' Coronation ' and ' Pinkie '.

The red cups show more strongly the influence of the variety poetarum.

' Acme ', ' Ace of Diamonds ' and ' Steadfast ' are good examples, and the new, and therefore costly, ' Smyrna ' gained an Award of Merit in 1933 and is rightly worthy of it. ' Ditty ' (Chapman) is a borderline flower with an orange eye rimmed with red.

A few forms exist, and I hope more will come, in which the red ring has been softened down to a light coral colour that is very pleasing.

' Mallard ', raised by Mr. A. M. Wilson, is a lovely, small flower, its ring more orange than red. ' Esterelle ', from the same raiser, has a very thin, picotee-like edge.

' Tiddlywinks ', from Mr. P. D. Williams, is one of the neatest, roundest flowers ever seen, and has a flat lemon-yellow cup edged with light coral. It is small enough to wear in a buttonhole if it were not too beautiful for such cruel treatment.

N. poeticus has produced double forms from early times. The first of these would probably be that described and figured by Clusius in the *Historia*, which had a second whorl of six perianth segments springing from the inside of the unbroken, red-edged corona.

He grew another with as many as twenty segments, heard of one with sixty-four, and figured and described one much like the double form of the present day known as the Gardenia-Flowered Narcissus. C. de Pas has a beautifully drawn figure of a form with nineteen perianth segments, which he says show traces of yellow among the whiteness and stamens in the centre.

Gerard mentions no double poeticus, but Johnson added the two figures from Clusius and extracts from his description. Parkinson figures one form showing no coronal portions, and describes two others. The first he seems to have grown, as he found that when crowded and starved it produced flowers ' very little double and almost single ', but if he set his roots single the flowers would be goodly and double. The other two are described in a manner so reminiscent of Clusius and C. de Pas that they may well be paraphrases and afford no evidence of direct knowledge.

N. poeticus plenus, the Gardenia Narcissus and N. albus plenus odoratus of catalogues, is a wonderfully good plant where it grows well, and unfortunately that is by no means everywhere. Deep and rich soil in orchards and an equable climate help it to thrive, but when it meets with a check from changes of temperature, cold nights or hot and dry days during its growing season, the buds frequently become blind and the flowers do not develop inside the inflated bags of the spathes.

In some western districts it is a valuable market plant, flowering in the latter part of May when all others are over, and is so white that it is a most useful florist's flower for wreaths and church vases.

Several new varieties have been raised lately. The best is Mr. Engleheart's ' White Rose ', which received a F.C.C. in 1933 and is figured facing p. 128 in *The Daffodil Year Book* of that year, unfortunately from an old and rather transparent specimen; a smaller figure from better specimens is in Mr. Calvert's *Daffodil Growing*, Pl. 202.

It resulted from the self-pollination of a poeticus flower which Mr. Engleheart noticed had one petalloid anther. The seedlings produced several doubles, and

' White Rose ' is the best.   ' Carnation ', its sister,
is not so purely white, but its slightly sulphur flowers
are as fully double and as regularly formed as those
of a Border Carnation.

' Daphne ' has a more exciting history.   It appeared
suddenly about 1908 in a large batch of poeticus
ornatus forced for market by Mr. F. Culpin of Spald-
ing.   It was not noticed until the flowers had been cut
and were being bunched, so it was impossible to mark
the bulb that season.   Mr. Culpin, realising the value
of a double form of such an early-flowering variety,
had the whole of this forced stock planted in the field,
and after two years he was rewarded by the reappear-
ance of the precious novelty.   A large stock of over
1,400 bulbs was worked up and passed into the hands
of Mr. George Monro for £1,000, and it was named
after his daughter.   It is a beautifully formed flower,
not too double and with large overlapping segments,
which create a fascinating play of light and shade that
I long to paint.   However, since it received the F.C.C.
at the Narcissus Committee in 1924 I have not again
set eyes upon it.   It is well shown in a photograph
reproduced in *The Gardeners' Chronicle* for May 10th,
1924.

XVIII

Autumnal Species

N. viridiflorus of Schousboë. Schousboë was a Danish
botanist who published a book on the vegetation of
Morocco in 1800. In it he states that he found N.
viridiflorus growing spontaneously on the coast of
Barbary and on the neutral ground between Gibraltar
and St. Roque. It is still plentiful in this European
locality, but is more widely spread in Morocco and
Oran.

It is therefore one of those interesting species which
are clearly of African origin, and occur in Europe
only in restricted localities along the shores of the
Mediterranean, proclaiming a former land connection
between the two Continents. Other examples may
be found in the Palmetto (Chamaerops humilis), Crocus
Salzmannii, Narcissus serotinus and, among animals,
the Barbary Ape.

John Parkinson was the first to mention and to figure
' the greene Autumne Jonquilia ', as he named it
beneath its portrait. This is Fig. 6 on p. 93 of his
Paradisus, and is both interesting and important. It
is interesting because it was most likely drawn from
a living or dried specimen for this book, whereas
most of the figures are rough copies from woodcuts
used in earlier works. It is of importance because it
represents the corona as having an entire margin
instead of being divided to its base in six places to
form six lobes, each of which is slightly emarginate.

All the specimens that I have examined showed the
six-lobed corona. The beautiful Pl. 1687 in the
Botanical Magazine for the year 1815 clearly shows the

lobes, and Herbert and all subsequent describers consider the six-lobed corona to be the typical form.

Haworth, the forerunner of Jordan in zeal for
creating genera, species and varieties, invented the
name Chloraster for a genus that should contain two
species, C. fissus (the cloven-cupped), which is founded
on the *Botanical Magazine* figure and description,
and C. integer (the entire-cupped), his only evidence for
which is Parkinson's description and figure.

Dean Herbert in his *Amaryllidaceae* questions the
propriety of recognising this form even as a variety
and writes: 'The existence of this variety with an
entire margin to the cup depends on the accuracy of
Parkinson's figure; and, as he does not state the margin
to be entire, I consider the figure to deserve very
little credit.'

It is clear that neither Haworth nor Herbert saw
reliable specimens of N. viridiflorus. For Haworth
in the Second Edition of his *Monograph* places an
asterisk against his two so-called species to signify
that plants so marked are 'unknown to Author', and
Herbert was doubtful whether the two-flowered
specimens from Tangiers, a portion of which he
represents in Fig. 28 of his Pl. 41, are viridiflorus or
obsoletus, as 'the colour of the flowers cannot be
ascertained'.

Herbert is not quite fair in writing that Parkinson
did not 'state the margin to be entire', for his description may imply that it was so. He wrote ' a small
round cup, or rather crowne', and those words may
mean that it was undivided. Parkinson's description
is so clear and correct in other points that it suggests
his having handled a specimen. It runs thus:

' This strange Rush Daffodil (I call it strange, not
onely because it differeth from all others of this kinde,
but also because there are but few in these parts that
have had it, and fewer that doe still enjoy it, in that

it is perished with all that had it) hath but one onely leaf, very long, rounded, and greene, in all that ever I saw growing, which beareth no flower while that greene leafe is fresh, and to bee seene; but afterwards the stalke riseth up, being like unto the former greene leafe, round, naked and greene up to the toppe, where two or three flowers breake forth out of a small thin skinne, every one consisting of six small and narrow greene leaves very sharpe pointed at the end, and as it were ending in a small pricke or thorne, in the middle whereof is a small round cup, or rather crowne, of the same colour with the leaves and stalke, which flower smelleth very sweete, somewhat like unto the rest of the Rush Daffodils: this sheweth not his flower untill October, and the frosts quickly following after their flowering cause them soone to perish.'

It may well be thought that he who observed the ' small pricke or thorne ' at the tip of each segment could not fail to notice and to record a six-lobed cup had it been present. On the other hand we should compare this description with those he applied to other small Narcissi. Thus, Fig. 4 on p. 89 shows two flowers with curious, irregularly triangular cups, which he describes as ' small and round like unto the cup or crowne of the least Rush Daffodil '. This is represented as Fig. 2 on the same page and shows a perfectly circular flat cup, divided into six equal portions by six dark radii which may represent slits or stripes of colour. At any rate this cup is unlike any known among Narcissi at the present time, and Herbert may be justified in regarding Parkinson's figure as deserving very little credit.

It would, however, be unwise to conclude that a form with entire margin to the cup has never existed. A useful work may be done by anyone who has the opportunity of examining the plant in its native habitat by looking for any variation in the lobing of the cup.

I have dealt with this minor point so fully because it shows how difficult it is to harmonise the views of older writers, and it is such a good example of the methods of the two kinds of botanists called lumpers and splitters.

Burbidge's Pl. 44 was drawn from specimens in the Kew Herbarium, and has been found fault with as representing the leaves and flowers as contemporaneous, which of course they truly are, but it seldom happens that a leaf and scape are found on the same bulb.

It is difficult to see in dried specimens whether the scape and leaf emerge from one and the same sheathing-leaf, or each from a separate one that does not rise above the cap of the tunic. I possess Burbidge's original sketch, and it shows, more clearly than the reproduction, traces of separate sheathing-leaves for each true leaf and scape.

N. viridiflorus possesses the unobliging disposition and habit of many African bulbs and has inherited characters that almost correspond to reflex actions in animals. Its yearly activity begins with the falling of the autumnal rains after a resting period enforced by drought or heat.

One of its peculiarities, shared so far as I know by only one other Narcissus, its close relative N. serotinus, is the extreme economy by which a flowering specimen wastes nothing on the production of a leaf. The scape remains green whether the seeds are formed or no, lengthens greatly and takes on the work of a leaf. As grown in England I have known the scape to be active and green well into August, but most likely in the heat of North Africa it ripens off much earlier. I have never seen a specimen bearing both leaf and scape, unless there happened to be two bulbs enclosed in a wrapping of old tunics and looking like one.

Scape and leaf are dark shining green, and nearly

as round as a rush, and so much alike that except for the remains of the spathe and withered flowers at the top of the former it is difficult to distinguish them. Strong bulbs produce leaves of over a foot in length, and some collected for me in marshy ground had leaves twice as large in diameter as those from dry places.

The bulbs from the marsh were found close to the surface, but normally they are at a depth of 4 to 6 inches and very difficult to dig out of the heavy clay in which they are found in Spain.

These deep bulbs are globose, but many that I have cultivated in more open soil show a tendency to grow long and narrow and rather irregular in outline, closely resembling, on a larger scale, the long bulbs formed by seedlings of many varieties of Narcissus when in their first and second seasons.

This shape probably assists them to descend, and its occurrence in full-grown bulbs of viridiflorus, when planted shallowly in dry ground, may be an inherited habit of descending to lower levels to obtain moisture, and also a hint of another primitive character retained by this strange plant.

The bulb also differs from others in the number of its scales, due to the reduction in number of foliar organs, which is even greater than in Galanthus, which has two leaves besides the sheathing-leaf. In N. viridiflorus, as Gay recorded for N. serotinus, flowering bulbs appear to have two sheathing-leaves, but the inner of these is an undeveloped leaf with a tubular base occasionally bearing a minute projection representing a rudimentary leaf-blade at the top; thus the number of bulb-scales formed annually is limited to two only. The same arrangement is found in non-flowering bulbs in which no scape is produced and only the bases of the sheathing-leaf and true leaf are available to grow into bulb-scales.

The scales are unusually thick and fleshy, and some

13

of them persist for more than one season before becoming scarious to form the dark brown tunics which
glisten like those of Jonquils. The upper tubular
portion is produced to reach the ground-level in those
that are deeply buried and serves to keep a clear
passage-way through the stiff, baked soil for the rapid
uprising of the tender scape at the advent of the first
autumnal rain. The same applies to Crocus aureus
and C. Sieberi, both of which have long sheathing-
leaves very similar in appearance to those of N. viridiflorus and serve the same purpose when growing
in the stiff clay from which I dug them in Greece.
They would be more necessary in the Narcissus, as
the sharp-pointed leaves of the Crocus, bound together
by the sheathing-leaves, produce a very powerful
boring machine, whereas in the Narcissus the toughened
tip of the spathe, even with the assistance of the
pointed perianth segments of the uppermost flower
tightly packed within it, must be a far less powerful
instrument, only able to force its way up a kind of
chimney in the well-baked soil when the cavity is
kept open by the tubular sheathing-leaves.

The scape, pedicels, ovary and the backs of the
perianth segments appear to the naked eye of a dull,
rather glaucous green. A strong lens will show that
the bluish tint is due to a powdering of minute white
specks over a very dark green background. On the
inner surface of the perianth segments these white
dots are more irregular in shape, rougher and mealy
in appearance and slightly crystalline.

The green coloration of the perianth and corona
is the greatest peculiarity of the plant, and is found
in no other species, though the tube and the back
of the perianth segments of many forms are more or
less tinged with green, as in Bulbocodium, Van
Sion, alpestris and others. A ring of green occurs,
with a very beautiful effect, in the base of the cups

of many lately raised forms of Leedsii and poeticus, but is unknown on the inner surface of perianths except as a result of injury.

Though this remarkable Narcissus is so small and so difficult to grow in England that it can never be a popular plant in our gardens, it is so extremely interesting botanically and so delightfully fragrant that it is worthy of the attention of the ' curious '. It increases and flowers fairly well in some seasons. I grow it at the back of an unheated frame planned for Crocus species. It is unreliable and pernickety even there, and in some seasons the bulbs have thrown up neither leaves nor scapes, but when lifted in the following August were healthy and grew vigorously after being replanted. Good results have been obtained by growing them in pots and hanging these in the roof of a greenhouse to dry and ripen the bulbs during their resting season, in the same manner as is practised for Nerines.

Hybrid forms between N. viridiflorus and serotinus were found by G. Maw in 1883 near Gibraltar, and more abundantly in 1886 six miles from Tangier, where the two species grew intermixed. In *The Gardeners' Chronicle*, November 20th, 1886, p. 661, he recorded the later find, stating that the individuals varied greatly in their degree of resemblance to one or other parent. After the unusually hot and dry summer of 1933, Mr. J. E. Edwards of Government House, Gibraltar, was successful in finding specimens, after searching in vain for twelve seasons. Through his kindness I have been able to examine living specimens which mostly resembled N. viridiflorus in form and in their dark green scapes being uniformly powdered with white dots. On the other hand the six-cleft corona had rounded lobes showing no trace of emargination; they were of a dull greenish yellow like the flesh of a ripe greengage, and this colour spread out into the bases of the inner segments. All the six segments were nearly white, and what little coloration there was consisted of a slight staining more yellow than green in shade.

N. serotinus Linnæus (1753). This minute plant is the most widely spread of the Autumn-flowering species, being found in Southern Europe from Portugal to Greece, along the Mediterranean region of North Africa and in Palestine.

It is not likely that anyone would carry such an inconspicuous plant to distant lands, as has been the case with N. Tazetta; and the fact that Tazetta takes so readily to cultivated ground, while serotinus is only found in hot and dry positions and is extremely difficult to cultivate, must mean that its dispersal was perfectly spontaneous.

It must also have been a very ancient migration and formerly of a wider extent, as is shown by its occurrence on so many islands in the Mediterranean. It still survives on Corsica, Sardinia, Sicily, Malta, Crete, the Cyclades and the Ionian Isles, a relic of their connection with the mainland.

Its curious corona, insignificant flower and a tendency to bear more than one in an inflorescence stamp it as a primitive form.

Linnæus, following Loefling, describes it as one-flowered with a six-cleft corona, and the specimen in his herbarium agrees thereto. Though the greater number of plants produce one-flowered scapes, those with two flowers are not uncommon, and occasionally a very strong bulb is found bearing a three-flowered head. The corona is very short (only about 1 mm.) and shrinks in drying, so that it is difficult to observe at any time, but especially in dried specimens. All those that I examined in 1933 while fresh had only three lobes, but one specimen had one lobe of the corona divided in half and resembling two of the lobes of the six-cleft corona of N. viridiflorus. In October 1934, however, most of the bulbs that flowered in my frame and unheated greenhouse bore flowers having the corona six-cleft as described by Linnæus.

Herbert figured and described N. deficiens in the *Botanical Register*, vol. xxxiii., t. 22, Fig. 1, with the corona reduced to six mere rudiments which he could only see through a lens. It was either an unusually short-cupped form of N. serotinus or a very young stage of the flower. I find that in flowers not yet fully expanded the corona closely resembles the condition described by Herbert and that the higher anthers protrude for almost their whole length above the minute rim of coronal lobes, which are then of a greenish brown colour very much like that of N. elegans.

N. serotinus is of great interest in that it is apparently intermediate between N. viridiflorus and N. elegans in several characters which vary slightly in their degree of resemblance to one or other of those two species. Besides the variation of form and colour of the corona already noticed, the leaves have been described so differently by many botanists that I could not believe they were observing the same plant until I saw for myself in living specimens that all were right in stating that leaves of certain forms existed, and all were wrong in imagining they could not be of any other form than that they were describing. Bianca and Parlatore, followed by Gay, Coste and Battandier, declare them to be cylindric, junciform, or filiform. Post described those of the Syrian plant as ' filiform grooved at upper surface '. Grenier and Godron make them ' narrowly linear and nearly filiform, channelled on the upper surface ', which Gay considered would only fit N. elegans.

Before me as I write there is a living specimen from Jerez bearing a scape and also a leaf 2 mm. in width and deeply channelled the whole length of its upper surface. It is produced from within the same sheathing-leaf as the scape, which is a very rare occurrence. The channel was necessary when the two were pressed together in early stages, and has persisted. Among numerous other specimens from Jerez and Gibraltar, I have only seen two bearing a scape and leaf within the same sheathing-leaf.

Gay examined 162 specimens and found only 3 bearing leaf and scape. Old bulbs wrapped in many layers of tunics may produce both scape and leaf, but the leaf can be traced down to a lateral sheathing-leaf, denoting an offset bulb within the tunics.

Strong leaves generally show a very narrow groove or split in their upper surface, and those from very small immature bulbs are filiform.

The fact is that very few botanists have seen the leaves in living plants. Clusius declared that no leaves sprang from the bulbs and he could find no vestiges of any. Gay's correspondent at Oran, who cultivated some in a pot, wrote that 'when it flowers it bears no leaves; the young bulbs which do not flower have them '. Gay was the first to point out that N. serotinus is normally leafless, like N. viridi-florus, in flowering bulbs, and that all other writers except Clusius were wrong in believing that the plant is hysteranthous, producing leaves after the flower is over.

In both of these species the scapes lengthen considerably after the flowers fade, and whether seeds are produced or no, they remain green for a long period and function as leaves. Bulbs which are not flowering produce their leaf at the same time as the scapes appear from others, and doubtless when growing among other plants, especially among grass, and without flower or seedpod, both scapes and leaves must be very inconspicuous.

A very curious error has existed for more than three hundred years as to the form of the scape of N. serotinus. It was believed that, unlike all other members of the genus, it possessed an articulated flower stalk, divided into several portions by solid nodes like those in the stems of grasses.

The draughtsman who prepared the woodcut for the publisher Plantin of Antwerp seems to have started the heresy. This block was first used in Clusius's *History of Spanish Plants*[1] in 1576 and again in his *Historia* in 1601, afterwards by Lobel and in Johnson's Gerard and elsewhere. It shows two bulbs, one with two scapes each bearing a single flower, the other one a seedpod. The bulbs are well drawn and show the tunics that cover the neck with loose upper ends more or less turned outward, as often happens in a dried specimen. In the flowering specimen these are followed by what seems to have been intended for a series of six sheathing-leaves enclosing the scape right up to the spathe, and most of these have at least one side ending in a projecting point. The shorter scape which bears the half-opened flower has only three with points, but above those the outlines of the stalk are joined across by dark bands in five places. The plant in seed has no such divisions above the sheathing-leaves.

The type specimen of N. serotinus in Linnæus's herbarium has the base of the scape divided by three thickened rings, looking wonderfully like the nodes of a Bamboo stem on a minute scale. Gay was the first to note that the scapes of N. serotinus and elegans in the process of drying occasionally shrink unevenly, leaving wrinkles with node-like edges at irregular distances.

I have watched these wrinkles forming in drying specimens, especially when attached to the bulb. The

---

[1] *Rariorum aliquot stirpium per Hispanias observatarum historia.*

upper portion becomes dry and shrunken down to a certain point, below which the stalk remains plump and green for a longer period, being fed by the still living bulb, but later shrinks and dries for another short length. The junction of the dry and green portions does not shrink as much as those above and below it and is left as a protruding ring.

The same formation can often be seen in living bulbs when dry after lifting, sometimes in the scarious upper portions of scales wrapping the neck and more often in the dried base of an old scape if one remains at the top of the neck.

I believe, therefore, that Plantin's draughtsman drew from dried specimens, slightly exaggerating the points of tunics and sheathing-leaves and failing to understand the nature of the node-like wrinkles. The original figure was copied, another stalk added and the errors exaggerated so much that the nodes grew into a greater number of sheathing-leaves with longer and more recurved points.

This later block was used in Tabernaemontanus's *Kreuterbuch* in 1588, and in Gerard's *Herbal* of 1597. This was bad enough, but worse was to follow, for by the time Parkinson had added his copy to the crude collection of caricatured plants in his *Paradisus*, the ' Little White Autumne Daffodil ' possessed the flower of a Gentian on the stalk of a Carnation. Miller and Tenore described the scape of serotinus as knotted, and Haworth went so far as to call it the Knotty stalked autumnal, on the evidence of Parkinson's figure and Linnæus's specimen, and he questions the propriety of its inclusion in the genus Hermione because of its anomalous nodose scape.

Dean Herbert wrote in his *Amaryllidaceae*: ' On examination of many specimens, it appears that the knots exist in a very small proportion of them, quite irregular in their number and position, not being

articulations but swellings of the scape, and I appre-
hend they must have been occasioned by the deposit
of the egg and larva of some very small insect.' He
figured three of these swellings in Fig. 30 on Pl. 41
as seen by him on a Sardinian specimen.

I examined many living specimens from Spain for
traces of any form of gall, and found nothing of the
kind, but on a few scapes there were small brown
marks that might have been caused by a puncture
made by an insect, and I am convinced that the excrescences seen by Herbert were wrinkles caused by
uneven shrinkage and that the fabulous belief in an
articulated scape may be abandoned.

Clusius named the species serotinus, the late-flowering, and Herbert in *Amaryllidaceae*, p. 327, has explained
so fully why the accent should be on the o and not
on the i that I have never dared to pronounce it otherwise, though serótinus sounds less pleasing than
seroti'nus. Clusius wrote that 'we may also say the
lesser autumnal, for I think we can hardly find a smaller
Narcissus'. It is not so small in all its parts as N.
minutiflorus, but is perhaps the most slender as regards
stem.

The flower is of better form and wider in the segments
than that of elegans, brilliantly white with a touch of
bright orange on the tiny coronal lobes. The scent is
strong and very sweet, at first rather like that of Jasmine,
but, as in certain forms of Tazetta, it has a suggestion of
soot if smelt at strongly; and Mr. Edwards has noticed
that a bunch of it gathered at Gibraltar gave out a
strong soot-like scent in a closed room.

The scape examined through a lens will be seen
to be powdered with minute white dots, like those
of N. viridiflorus, but whereas in that they are scattered
thickly and evenly over the whole surface, in serotinus
they are only found on the six flattened spaces which
alternate with six series of three slightly raised, dark

green, vertical ribs which run up the scape and into the spathe, forming its veins.

The tube is grooved with six furrows; the rounded, raised portion between each is marked with three green lines and corresponds with each segment of the perianth. The grooves are deeper and wider in the upper two-thirds of the tube and are there of a light orange colour, which together with the orange inner surface of the tube helps to brighten up this charming little blossom.

When more than one flower is borne on a scape, the tubes of secondary flowers are flattened on the side that was pressed against the ovary of the principal flower in the spathe in the same manner as in Tazetta forms. This pressure also affects the corona so that it becomes oval instead of circular.

Mr. Edwards tells me in a letter that he dug up twelve bulbs of N. serotinus on October 24th just as they were coming into flower, and that every bulb was lying horizontally in the ground and all root growth tended upwards as though to benefit from the very first of the early autumnal rains.

Burbidge's Pl. 46 was drawn from specimens in the Kew Herbarium and shows variously cleft cups and the groove in the leaf. Pl. 82 in the first volume of Desfontaines's *Flora Atlantica* was drawn by Redouté and, by the flattened appearance of the flowers, most likely from dried specimens, but only the left-hand, leafless plant is N. serotinus. There is a good outline figure in Coste's *Fl. de France*, vol. iii., Fig. 3559.

Sir W. Thiselton-Dyer, when identifying the plants of Theophrastus's *Enquiry* for Sir Arthur Hort's translation, thought that his autumnal Narcissus or Leirion represented N. serotinus. As Clusius pointed out in the *Historia*, p. 163, it is probably the plant he named Narcissus persicus, but now known as Sternbergia macrantha. The plant described by Theophrastus has leaves broader than those of Asphodel, a grass-green stalk, and a large oblong fruit from which men collect seeds to sow as well as planting its large fleshy root. Nothing of this agrees with N. serotinus, but would fit the Sternbergia, which might have been brought to Greece by those scientifically trained men taken by Alexander to the East. If afterwards grown in gardens, the seeds of such an uncommon and showy plant would be likely to be collected and sown, but not those of a plentiful and insignificant native.

N. elegans. Spach was the first to use the combination N. elegans in 1846 for the Hermione elegans of Haworth's *Monograph* (1831) and of Herbert's *Amaryllidaceae* (1837). Link called it N. autumnalis in 1835, Gussone N. Cupanianus in 1842 and Bossier N. oxypetalus in 1843.

This autumnal species occurs in Italy, Sicily and North Africa, and has been frequently confused with N. serotinus. Most of the Narcissi make poor specimens in herbaria through shrinking and fading, and these small-flowered forms are annoyingly prone to both evil habits.

They are difficult to cultivate and to gather in the wild when out of flower, therefore leaves and fruit are poorly represented in herbarium specimens, and botanists must be forgiven for loading this humble plant with so many names.

The earliest figure was published in 1576 in Clusius's *History of Spanish Plants*. It was used again in the Flemish Edition of Lobel's *Kruydtboeck* and his album of illustrations called *Icones Stirpium*, both of which were published in 1581 by Plantin of Antwerp, who had these woodcut blocks prepared to illustrate the works of Clusius, Lobel and others, and the same figure not infrequently appeared under different names. Lobel called it N. minor serotinus medio croceus. Johnson used the block again in his enlarged edition of Gerard's *Herbal*. It is a good figure, showing an entire plant with a one-flowered scape and five leaves, as well as an enlarged flower and leaf by the side. The flat upper surface of the leaf is clearly displayed, marking it as N. elegans.

In Parkinson's *Paradisus*, N. albus Autumnalis medio obsoletus, the white Autumn Daffodill with a sullen crowne, is figured on p. 89, Fig. 4. This is a poor copy of the good figure on p. 22 of the *Theatrum Florae*. The coronas in both flowers are not circular, but compressed and elongated on one side. This is characteristic of both elegans and serotinus, but is usually found only in the secondary or third flower as the result of pressure from the ovary of the superior flower while wrapped in the spathe.

Tabernaemontanus used a different block in his *Kreuterbuch* of 1588, as N. 16 serotinus albus. It is one of those acquired by John Norton to illustrate Gerard's *Herbal* of 1597. The eight flat leaves and starry twisted perianth depict N. elegans, but neither Gerard nor Johnson knew the living plant. The former called it N. minor serotinus and described it as ' a faire white flower having in the middle a ringe or yellow circle, it flowereth later than the others in Aprill and May ', and Johnson repeats this without any of his customary comments exposing the mistakes of ' Our Author '. So it is clear that he knew no better. The description of the corona as ' a ringe or circle ' is further evidence of their ignorance. It is an accurate description of the draughtsman's two concentric circles but not of the living conical corona.

Redouté's drawing, Pl. 82, in Desfontaines's *Flora Atlantica*, contains both serotinus and elegans under the name N. serotinus. The smaller bulb bears a one-flowered scape and no leaf; the larger, two flat leaves and a seven-flowered scape, which is unmistakably elegans. In the text the small plant is regarded as a younger bulb and a variety of the larger.

Bertoloni so late as 1839 failed to distinguish them in his *Flora Italica*. Haworth in his *Monograph* (1831) used the name elegans for the two plants in the *Flora Atlantica* plate, because he considered they were not the serotinus of Linnæus's herbarium or of the *Species Plantarum*, as they had smooth instead of three-jointed scapes! He made a separate species, obsoleta, for Parkinson's wretched copy of the *Theatrum Florae* plate, calling it the white leafy autumnal.

It is strange that, although N. elegans was distinguished from serotinus by Clusius and Lobel and correctly represented by three contemporary woodcuts, Herbert was the first to detect the mistakes of his predecessors; but, having only dried specimens and figures to go by, he did not disentangle the confusion.

Gay must have the honour of making matters clear in his ' Recherches sur la Famille des Amaryllidacées ', in *Ann. Sci. Nat. Botaniques*, Series 4, ix., 2, 1859. He examined a great number of specimens and his conclusions can be summarised thus:

Characters common to both species:
1. Autumnal-flowering.
2. Absence of a mother-leaf at the base of the scape.
3. A cylindrical scape, of even outline in life, but drying in unequal portions and forming ridges resembling nodes.

Differences:
N. elegans, leaves produced before the flowers, two or more, with flat blades channelled on the upper face, corona generally conical and entire.

N. serotinus, flowering bulbs very rarely bear a leaf, non-flowering bulbs seldom more than one, leaves appearing at the same time as the scape, mostly filiform, corona three- to six-cleft.

After the unusually hot summer of 1933 both serotinus and elegans flowered freely, and I was able to examine and compare them and to add some points to Gay's observations.

In elegans the leaves were produced two or three weeks before the flower scapes, and were 5 to 6 mm. wide at flowering time, with concave upper surfaces and four strong ribs on the convex back.

The flower measures 4 to 5 cm. across, the green tube is 1 to 5 cm. long.

The spathe shows two deep green, longitudinal bands connected by wider portions of membrane and remains green during the flowering period. The cup is short and somewhat conical, being narrower at the mouth than at the base, circular in the principal flower and irregularly narrowed on one side in secondary flowers on the same scape, like the shape shown in the figure in *Theatrum Florae*.

The rim is obscurely six-lobed, when young of a dull, greenish brown like the flesh of a ripe greengage, but turns to a dull orange before fading. It has a curious roughened exterior due to minute crystalline papillæ.

The perianth spreads horizontally at first and reflexes slightly when mature. The segments twist considerably and in the end resemble a child's toy windmill. The flowers give out a strong scent resembling that of Night-scented Stock, but with an additional odour which suggests tar or creosote. The bulbs I have came from Morocco many years ago. They have increased in number in an unheated frame, but seldom flower.

Herbert adopted Haworth's obsoleta, founded solely on Parkinson's figure and description. He read a different meaning into the word obsoletus from that of Parkinson and Haworth, taking it to mean *absence of a corona* instead of *worn-out coloration*. Parkinson translated it as *sullen* and describes the crown as ' of a yellow colour at the bottom but towards the edge of a dunne or sullen colour '. In Rea's *Flora* of 1665, p. 130, we read of a ' dark sullen violet colour ', and Gerard and Coles used the equivalent term *overworn* for dull or apparently faded colours.

It is evidently not the rudimentary form of the corona but its dark colouring that Parkinson alluded to. Herbert's figure in his *Amaryllidaceae*, Pl. 42, Fig. 6, drawn from a dried specimen from Tangiers, in Bentham's herbarium, shows a two-flowered head, a large bulb and one flat leaf. The same drawing appears again in the *Botanical Register* for 1847, vol. xxxiii., t. 22. In the text he wrote: ' A Narcissus without a cup seems an anomaly, but Fig. 3 represents a dry specimen from Tangiers, which seems to me to be Parkinson's N. medio obsoletus.'

N. elegans with its flat leaves and many-flowered scapes approaches the Tazetta group and may well be a link in the chain of their evolution. A further step is provided in N. aequilimbus of Zerapha, bulbs of which were sent to Herbert from Malta. He figured one of these on Pl. 48 and described it in the supplement at the end of his *Amaryllidaceae*.

The leaves are as wide as those of the small wild type of Tazetta; the scape bears three flowers with white segments and a pale yellow, shallow cup $\frac{1}{16}$ inch long. The most remarkable feature is found in the outer and inner segments being of nearly equal width.

Battandier and Trabut in the *Flore de l'Algérie* mention, as N. intermedius of Gay, a supposed hybrid between N. serotinus and N. elegans, with characters that vary as to their likeness to one or other of their parents.

Gay regarded it as variety B of elegans, but described it (*Ann. Sci. Nat. Bot.*, Series 4, vol. ix., Pl. 2, p. 91, 1859) as intermediate, agreeing with elegans in having a single leaf, two-flowered scape and conical undivided corona, but with serotinus in the form of its perianth segments. He connects it with Herbert's figures of Hermione obsoleta and Schousboë's description of N. serotinus.

If these intermediate forms were known to Desfontaines, it would account for his placing the extreme forms, which we regard as elegans and serotinus, under one name on Pl. 82 of his *Flora Atlantica*.

XIX

BULBOCODIUM

THE GREAT variability of *N. Bulbocodium* in size, form
and coloration makes it difficult to define any form as
a distinct variety.

Mr. Tait communicated his observations of wild
forms in Portugal to the Scientific Committee of the
Royal Horticultural Society in 1887.[1]

He found a large form, perhaps conspicuus or
serotinus, in marshy ground and sandy pinewoods,
along with a smaller form varying from a rich orange
to pale yellow. He believed the variations were due
to environment, as he found larger kinds transplanted
to a dry position were reduced in size in the following
year. On higher ground in Northern Portugal small
forms with rush-like, twisted and drooping leaves
occurred, but at 3,000 feet in the Jerez Mountains the
variety nivalis with erect leaves, and flowers varying
from a rich yellow to pale sulphur, was prevalent.
Mr. Tait found the length of the styles so variable that
he considered it an unreliable character for classifica-
tory purposes.

It is not surprising, therefore, that in addition to
Bulbocodium thirteen other names have been published representing species with yellow flowers.

N. Bulbocodium is Linnæus's name for the Ps.-N.
juncifolius 2 flavo flore of Clusius's *Historia*, p. 166.
The accompanying figure shows the back and front of
two flowers, a seedpod and upright leaves. It was also
used by Lobel and in Johnson's Gerard. Linnæus
obtained this ridiculous specific name from Clusius's

---

[1] Reported in *The Garden*, vol. xxi., p. 360.

14

remark that some think it to be the Bulbocodium of Theophrastus. For the history of the mistaken reading that produced this word see page 13 of Chapter I. He gave as the distinguishing characters the corona cone-shaped (turbinate), of largest size and the pistil and stamens curved.

Salisbury in the *Transactions of the Horticultural Society* for 1812 proposed a separation from Ajax under the generic name Corbularia.[1] He provided no description of the genus, and Haworth was the first to do so, in his *Revisio* in 1819, and, as in his later *Monograph*, he made the curvature of the stamens and pistil the principal character.

Haworth divided Corbularia into two sections, the first with white and the other with yellow flowers. He never saw a white-flowered form, as shown by the asterisks in the Second Edition of his *Monograph*. Nevertheless he conjured up two species with the help of Clusius and Parkinson, giving misleading references in both cases.

C. cantabrica he founded on Clusius's description and figure on p. 166 of the *Historia*, referring to it as ' f. 2 '. It is the second *figure* on that page, but is Pseudo-narciss. juncifol., iii., albo flor. in title and description.

De Candolle in *Les Liliacées* in 1816, and Haworth later, seem to have derived this name from the statement of Clusius that John Mouton of Tournai sent him drawings of rush-leaved Narcissi dug up some years previously in the passes of Cantabria by someone returning from Gallicia. Cantabria is the classical name for the Biscayan Provinces of Spain and especially of Asturias, the Cantabrian Mountains being a part of the range extending from Galicia to the Pyrenees, and forming the southern boundary of that province.

Nyman and Willkomm give the Pyrenees as a locality

---

[1] Corbula in Latin is a ' little basket '.

for C. cantabrica, but only on the authority of Clusius
and Kunth, and the latter gives no independent observations.

Mrs. Loudon in her *Bulbous Plants* makes it a
native of Biscay and abundant in the passes of the
Pyrenees; another version of Clusius's statement.

Burbidge calls C. cantabrica the Cambridge Narcissus, mistaking Cantabria for Cantabrigia, and says
that the name ' originated from its having been grown
about 1588 by a Master Nicholas Belson, sometime
of King's College in Cambridge as noted by Gerard '.
Gerard's *Herbal*, published in 1597, contains no mention
of a white Hoop Petticoat, and though Johnson added
Clusius's figure and part of his description he does
not mention Master Belson.

Clusius describes his No. 111 as ' candidum omnino ',
and the widely spread corona of the figure resembles
that of the white plant. Otherwise it might be thought
he had the sulphur-coloured citrinus in mind, for the
leaves in his figure are too numerous and wide for the
white-flowered plant.

It is hard to believe that the white Hoop Petticoat
was ever found so far to the north as Cantabria. It is
now only to be found in the extreme South of Spain,
the Balearic Isles and North Africa.

It may be that the traveller brought bulbs of it
from much further south, in fact from his starting-
point *Gallicia* (as spelt by Clusius with two l's), a
form of Gallaecia, the modern Tarragona, which is
opposite the Balearic Isles; and that neither Mouton
nor Clusius realised that the white-flowered bulbs
were not collected in the Cantabrian Mountains at
the same time as the yellow-flowered ones.

The white Hoop Petticoat still occurs in Spain on
the eastward side of Gibraltar. Colonel Enever Tod
sent me specimens in 1932 and tells me that it grows
in stony scree, generally among small bushes and

in shade, whereas the yellow N. Bulbocodium prefers open exposures and nearly always grows on a rock, often mixed with Scilla monophylla, especially on flat ledges, where their roots form a thick mat. The white plant, on the contrary, is scattered singly, or two or three together. It is found in heathy ground in the Balearic Isles and abundantly in North Africa, in Oran and on the coast and in the interior of Algeria.

Haworth's second species, albicans, is imaginary and, as Herbert pointed out, was founded on an erroneous reference to Parkinson's *Paradisus*, p. 106, Fig. 4. There are no figures on p. 106, and Fig. 4 of the following page is the double eystettensis, a copy of that in *Theatrum Florae*.

Parkinson describes Ps. juncifolius albus on p. 106 by what is mostly a translation of Clusius supplemented by mentioning that the flowers sometimes decline to a pale colour and the seed is like that of other Rush Daffodils but smaller, and he may not have seen a living plant.

The white Hoop Petticoat has received two other specific names besides cantabrica.

Dunal used N. Clusii for it in *Mem. Acad. Sci. Montpellier* in 1847. Durieu used C. monophylla at about the same date in Duchartre, *Rev. Bot.*, ii., 425, a work which appeared in parts during 1846 and 1847. The question as to which author launched his name first could only be settled by referring to the wrappers showing the exact date of publication, which I have been unable to do.

However, the name that should be used depends upon whether the plant is regarded as a separate species or as a variety of N. Bulbocodium.

If it is considered a species of Narcissus, De Candolle's name N. cantabricus would stand, as he used it in vol. viii. of *Les Liliacées* in 1816, in the list of species of Narcissus given under t. 486, and it is therefore the earliest specific name used in conjunction with Narcissus.

If it is treated as a variety, the valid name is that chosen by the first author to describe it as a variety of N. Bulbocodium.

In this case it is J. G. Baker who described N. Bulbocodium var. monophylla in *The Gardeners' Chronicle* in 1869 and afterwards corrected the spelling to *monophyllus* in the text accompanying t. 5831 of the *Botanical Magazine* for 1870.

This beautiful plant is too tender for outdoor cultivation in most parts of England, but is a veritable gem for the Alpine house and for growing in pans. The pure white flowers are beautifully crystalline when they are young and equally admirable when the corona becomes thinner, and portions between the ribs are almost as transparent as the finest lawn.

The bulbs can stand any amount of drying, and, as Dr. Masters recorded in *The Gardeners' Chronicle*, May 14th, 1870, bulbs that had been kept in a herbarium for twenty-two years were found to be alive, and being placed in a greenhouse they flowered the following year.

The African form generally produces no more than one leaf; some sent to me from Spain had two or three.[1]

A good figure can be found in *Bot. Mag.*, t. 5831, drawn by Fitch. Burbidge's Pl. 2 is good, but his Pl. 33 B shows a smaller, poorer form with slightly tinted flowers; a pen-and-ink sketch by Burbidge appeared in *The Garden*, February 10th, 1883, and another illustration from an excellent photograph on September 21st, 1901.

[1] In his *Contrib. Fl. Afr. Nord.*, fasc. 19, no. 1338 (1932), Dr. Maire has described as N. Bulbocodium subspec. tananicus a white Hoop Petticoat which is chiefly distinguished by its 3 to 5 erect leaves comparatively thick and rigid.

C. de Pas may have copied the figure in the *Hortus Floridus*, Hyems 9, from Clusius, there is so much likeness between them.

The white Bulbocodium was crossed with N. Tazetta by Sir Michael Foster and described with a figure in *The Garden*, February 11th, 1905, as N. Montaz.

For garden purposes it is well to divide the yellow forms of N. Bulbocodium into two, the pale lemon-coloured variety citrinus, and the deep yellow, which latter can be divided again according to early and late flowering, though it is impossible to draw a hard-and-fast line of division, because there are so many intermediate forms.

Citrinus is mostly found in marshy ground, where it produces larger flowers on taller stalks than any other form. This is well illustrated in *The Garden*, vol. xxviii., p. 243, 1883, by a drawing made by F. W. Burbidge from a plant grown by Miss Jekyll; but sulphur-coloured forms are found among the smaller deep yellow ones in high ground in Asturias and elsewhere.

In England var. citrinus will grow in moist ground that is not water-logged, but better still in cool, mossy woodland and grassy slopes as at Wisley, where it sows itself freely and varies endlessly in width of leaf and the form of the corona, which in many is oval or asymmetrically curved at the mouth.

There is no good coloured figure of it. The *Bot. Mag.* Fig. B in t. 6473 of N. Graellsii comes nearest to it, but is painted a pale sickly green, perhaps due to a change in the pigment used, and the anthers protrude considerably more than is usual with citrinus. The variety Graellsii grows in the mountains of Castille.

A very beautiful sulphur form was brought from the High Atlas in 1927 by the late Sir William Lawrence, and has flourished in the open ground at Burford,

flowering earlier than the European citrinus. Further
differences are found in the very narrow leaves and
flatter, more widely spread mouth of the corona and
protruding pistil, in which it closely resembles monophyllus and possibly should be regarded as a yellow
form of it. Coming from an elevation of 5,000 feet, it
promises to be hardy where the early-growing leaves
can be protected. Two excellent photographs of it
are reproduced in *The Gardeners' Chronicle* for March
14th, 1931, p. 205, showing plants at home on the High
Atlas and equally happy at Burford.

The best deep yellow forms for the garden are those
that flower rather late. One of them is the old garden
favourite generally known as conspicuus. It is beautifully figured in Sweet's *Brit. Fl. Gard.*, vol. iv.
of the Second Series, t. 326, but not so successfully in
Fig. C of Burbidge's Pl. 1. The neat upright leaves
and the green markings on the tube and the backs of
the segments give an extra touch of smartness to the
stiff, bright yellow Hoop Petticoats. It flowers late
in April or in May.

On t. 164 of the same work the largest form is shown
as Corbularia serotina of Haworth. He adopted this
name from Parkinson's Fig. 8 on p. 107, and connected
it with the turgida of Salisbury and t. 8 of the *Botanical
Magazine*. It has longer and wider leaves, and flowers
of a purer yellow with very large, smooth petticoats.
Burbidge's Fig. A on Pl. 1 resembles it, but the
colourist has been rather too lavish with green stripes
on this plate. Redouté's t. 24 in *Les Liliacées* is a
beautiful drawing.

I have lately received plants of what appears to be
this form collected in Portugal, where near the coast
it grows in clumps, but further inland a smaller-
flowered form is found singly as if only increased from
seed.

Salisbury's tenuifolius is a narrow-leaved, early-flowering form. The figure in Sweet's *British Flower Garden* shows it with a six-lobed corona and long, narrow spreading leaves. Redouté's drawing, t. 486 in *Les Liliacées*, is without distinct lobes. The text describes it as flowering in February in Spain and early in March at Montpellier.

A similar form grows between Gibraltar and Algeciras among the boulders where a light humous soil occurs, chiefly formed of decayed leaves of the Cork Oak. There they flower from January onwards.

XX

Cultivation

IF A motto were sought to be inscribed in large letters at the entrance to a Daffodil garden, could a better be found than the terse Arab proverb, ' Dig on a hundred days, water on one '? or, seeing that we do not water Daffodils in the open ground, should we tamper with the original text and write ' none '?

Narcissi root early in the Autumn, and plunge their roots down to a great depth where well-tilled, friable soil permits. They require plentiful moisture throughout their growing season, but stagnant water is almost always destructive. Badly drained soils frequently produce ' basal rot ' and a form of ' stripe '.

The percolation of water from melting snows through a steep alpine meadow's gritty or shaly loam during the flowering period is quite a different matter to a water-logged bed on the level. Water is often held back on such a bed by an unbroken soil pan which could be remedied by careful digging.

In any soil digging would do no harm. In light, sandy ground it is necessary to get something better than sand *down* as deep as the roots will go. In gravels it means getting something bad *out*, and stones represent that something. In heavy clay the introduction of humus, grit and air will do more good at a depth of 2 feet than at the surface. Therefore, dig. Even the fortunate man who has a parcel of ground with a deep and gritty loam for soil should not omit deep digging.

The more the ground is dug the better will be its disintegration to form what is known as a fine tilth, and nothing mellows soil better than exposing it to the action of sun and air.

Choice and new varieties should be grown in carefully prepared ground wherever special beds for a collection of Daffodils can be set aside for them alone.

In the average medium-sized garden this can be arranged most easily in some part of the kitchen garden. In more affluent and extensive estates perhaps a portion of good arable land could be annexed for a more important adventure.

In either case ground that has been used for a crop of early Potatoes is suitable. Narcissi will flourish in soils containing thoroughly mellowed humus, but fresh farmyard manure must never be used where it may come into contact with the bulbs.

The only instance in which fresh cowyard or stable manure could be of use would be in excessively light sand, and there it must be placed as a layer, so deeply that the roots of the bulbs would not reach it. Its work would be that of a sponge to retain moisture and not as a food.

Ground heavily manured for early Potatoes and thoroughly trenched afterwards should be in good condition for Daffodils by the following September. Where this perfect condition is unobtainable artificial manures could be used, and the safest and easiest to apply is bone meal. This can be used at the rate of 1 to 2 ounces to the square yard, and may be applied evenly on the surface and forked in before the bulbs are planted, or dusted over after planting and lightly raked in.

Basic slag is also used, and kainit is advisable for very light soils. Further advice and details will be found in Bulletin No. 44, *Narcissus Culture*, issued by the Ministry of Agriculture.

Bone meal, or steamed bone flour, can do no harm if not overdone, and can be used as a surface dressing

to beds that have not been lifted that season.   They act
gradually and slowly, and therefore the bulbs receive
nourishment throughout their period of growth and
are not overstimulated at any one period.

When choosing a site for the beds, one alongside
a path running approximately east and west is good.

The bed should be on the northern side of the path,
so that the flowers, which will all face to the sunniest
quarter, may be seen at their best from the path.   No
bed should exceed 4 feet in width, and ought only
to be of that width where access can be provided at
the back as well as the front, so that the centre of the
bed can be reached easily from either side.

If there is no edging of stones or Box, it is useful
to enclose the beds with wooden edging-boards which
have been tarred some time before being used.   This
will be found very advantageous in any position that
is not well drained, as it permits of raising the
surface of the bed a few inches above the natural
level.

As a rule a site should be selected in ground fully
open to sunlight.   The greater the shelter from north
and east or any other rough winds the better.   Partial
shade, from tall trees or buildings, thrown on the beds
at midday, or for some hours of the day, is advantageous, especially to white trumpets and any varieties
with red colouring.   Where perfect flowers are expected, screening with hurdles or Hessian stretched
on upright posts provides a condition de luxe beyond
the requirements of the ordinary amateur gardener.

If a bed is of great length it is advisable to make
cross gangways at intervals to prevent stepping on the
beds and to save one's legs from journeys round the
extremities.

Certainly place your labels in front so as to read
them from the path, and as a luxury, if not regarded
as a necessity, another set facing the gangway at the

back. This may save many journeys to the front and is a valuable second string to the bow should one label become illegible or lost.

In ordinary cases bulbs can be left in the beds three years, but the best blooms will generally be produced in the second season. This depends somewhat on the thickness of planting. For beds the rows should be at least 7 to 10 inches apart, and for the greatest advantage to the growth of the bulb each one should be at a distance of three times the diameter of the bulb from its neighbour.

If the beds are planted chiefly to provide flowers for cutting, a closer planting may be used. The depth of planting depends upon the nature of the soil and the variety of the Narcissus. A depth of 3 to 5 inches from the surface of the soil to the base of the bulb represents a useful average. Poeticus varieties and others which form small bulbs prefer shallower planting than trumpet varieties appreciate, and maximus benefits from a depth of 8 inches.

' Firetail ', ' Henry Irving ' and some kinds liable to basal rot in moist soils are greatly helped by a handful of coarse sand placed below and around the bulbs. In stiff soils any variety would appreciate a similar attention.

No hard-and-fast rule can be given for the best period for lifting bulbs, as it will vary in different localities and seasons and for distinct varieties.

The most favourable period should occur not earlier than mid-June and not later than July. The ideal moment is when the present season's roots are old enough to dry up and come away cleanly soon after lifting and before the roots of next season have started into growth, as happens if a heavy July thunderstorm soaks the ground after a spell of drought.

In most varieties this can be determined by the appearance of the leaves. As soon as they turn yellow, fall down, and begin to dry up the bulb should be ready for a period of drying and rest.

Poeticus varieties, and those with the greatest inheritance of poeticus characters, have little or no definite resting period, the old roots remaining active until the new ones are long and busy. It is of course better to destroy the last year's roots than to interfere with the arrival of the coming generation; therefore the earlier that poeticus varieties can be lifted, cleaned and replanted the better they will flourish. They should not remain out of the soil for a day longer than is necessary.

Lifting bulbs is a rather tedious job, unless the varieties are very precious and have greatly increased in number and quality in the past season, when the satisfaction of a lucrative harvest outweighs the monotony of careful labour. No one should hurry or become careless in lifting Daffodils. Stabs from a wildly directed fork, sudden exposure of any undue length to scorching sunshine, or bruises from being thrown roughly into a basket, can be the cause of many failures.

When handling bulbs, *place* them carefully in the tray, basket, bag, or soil—never *drop* them. To place means here to lay each down gently where it is to remain without releasing your hold until it is at rest. A well-ripened bulb should have its cells distended with sap richly stored with food. Any cell wall that is broken by a knock, a bump on the bottom of a wooden box or from one bulb against another, means the extrusion of stored moisture to form a nidus for moulds and a starting-point for decay and the entrance of eelworms.

Personally I prefer stiff paper bags or large flower pots for the reception of bulbs, one by one, as I lift them. These are easy to remove to shed or room as soon as they are filled.

Some leave the lifted bulbs on the surface of the soil to ripen, or place them in the shade under a mat. Both are unsafe practices at times, for heat may scorch them, and the small Narcissus Fly, Eumerus, is quick to discover and lay eggs on exposed bulbs.

The ideal rest-cure for lifted bulbs is to be laid out singly in wooden trays with wooden slat bottoms in a dry and airy shed or Apple-room.

Most of them benefit from a gentle cleaning. The oldest tunics, frayed at their edges and already loose, should be rubbed off; dry roots pulled away from the basal plate; and offsets that have a basal root-plate of their own, and are lightly joined to the mother-bulb at one side, can be separated; but no offset wrapped round by a complete tunic skin which also enwraps the mother should be removed.

It is useful to grade bulbs at this stage of cleaning. The terms in general use for grades of bulbs are:

Broody, a family party of old and young bulbs, generally capable of careful division.

Double-nosed, those with more than one flowering point enclosed in the outer tunics.

Rounds, flowering bulbs, round in shape and without any offsets. These are the most desirable grade to plant.

Wall-sided, parent bulbs from which the offsets have been removed on one or both sides, leaving such sides flattened, also used for large offsets with one flat side.

Chips, small bulbs and offsets most of which are not large enough to flower.

Chips may grow into flowering bulbs in their second season after planting and be lifted as small rounds.

Wall-sided bulbs should produce large-flowering rounds in their second season.

Double-nosed bulbs mostly become broody in the following season and then would be the better for a lifting.

In the pleasure garden it is not always possible
to trench or dig deeply where Daffodils are to be
planted in isolated clumps among shrubs or herbaceous
plants; but the more thoroughly the soil can be prepared
for them the better they will grow and the longer they
can be left without replanting. They are of great
use for providing colour early in the season between
plants that flower later. Drifts of tall varieties look
well planted in the spaces between Michaelmas Daisies,
towards the back of herbaceous borders; shorter
varieties naturally make a better show closer to the
edge.

'Citronella', 'White Queen', 'H. C. Bowles',
'Beryl', 'W. P. Milner'; the two cyclamineus hybrids
'February Gold' and 'Orange Glory'; 'Gyrfalcon',
'Eoster', 'Circlet', 'Undine', Jonquilla and odorus
are all suitable for the front row. Raisers are inclined
to cast away dwarf varieties nowadays, but plants
with short, stiff stems, of good colouring and a free
habit may some day be in great request when the public
finds that they are more useful in the garden than the
tall show flowers required for exhibition.

'Electra', a beautiful, citron yellow, self-coloured 2a,
is seldom grown, but is one of the best to give a sheet
of bloom when planted in generous drifts, as it was
grown at one time among Azaleas at Wisley.

The tallest stalk I know of is found in 'Hall Caine',
a soft yellow 2a raised by Van Waveren. 'Lord
Kitchener', 'White Lady', 'Evangeline' and 'Warlock' are long-legged creatures good for distant
effect.

Early-flowering varieties are of greater garden value
than the late-comers, as they are the first flowers to
cover up bare patches and fill them with colour after
the Crocuses have done their share. At no time do
Daffodils make a braver show than during the ten
days or so when the tall Crown Imperials rise out

from among groups and drifts of their cooler and paler colouring.

Where more formal effects are desired Daffodils in groups of about twenty to fifty may be planted with spaces between to be filled up with annuals or spreading herbaceous plants which will flower from May onward and grow out over the spaces from which the Daffodils have retired.

In gardens where Daffodils are desired for cutting in any quantity it is wise to grow some of the most suitable varieties in beds reserved for that purpose, so that those in which a show of growing flowers should be on view need not be preyed upon too heavily.

Flowers should be gathered before they are fully opened, the most favourable stage being when the bud is free from the spathe and the perianth is beginning to spring open. Most of those that have any red in their colouring will develop brighter tints if gathered before the sunlight has touched them. The pink-cupped Leedsii ' Suda ' and the red-cupped ' Helios ' and ' Kennack ' are, however, among the few kinds that colour well in the open.

The early morning and late afternoon are the best times of day to gather Daffodils. Their stems will generally be fresh and crisp then, and will snap easily without needing a knife. As soon as they are picked the broken end should be held upwards in the hand, the flower heads hanging straight downwards. This prevents the slimy sap from running out, the loss of which is likely to check the full development of the blossom, and certainly saves the clothing of the gatherer from unpleasant messiness.

If many flowers are to be gathered, a pail containing water should be at hand into which the cut stalks may be placed as soon as possible. A long, flat basket (the kind called a Munstead basket) is the second best contrivance to carry with one, and the flowers take little or no harm if laid flat in it and not left there for long before being placed in water.

If kept in a cool room for a day, or even two days, the buds should be perfectly developed and fit for arranging in vases. A cold, damp shed will delay the development for a day or so if desired, and a warm greenhouse will hasten it if the blooms are needed in a hurry.

Daffodils, like all other flowers, will last longer in good condition if their stems are rinsed in water in a large vessel previously to being placed in the clean water in the vase that is to contain them eventually; and in warm weather and hot rooms it is of course beneficial to change the water about every other day, and if the lower 3 inches only of the stem are immersed it is better than soaking any more of a surface intended to live in air and not under water.

Most people prefer to arrange Daffodils with their own leaves, or (in the case of valuable varieties from which it is not desirable to cut foliage) with leaves gathered from some commoner varieties such as the indestructible 'Princeps' and 'Van Sion'. I prefer to use something else, believing that the leaves set up decay sooner than the stems, and, defiling the water, hasten the wilting of the flowers. Bare twigs are extremely useful for supporting Daffodil blossoms in widemouthed vases, and if wisely chosen please me more then any other setting.

Their angular growths and good brown colouring contrast most pleasantly with the stiff green stems and brightly coloured flowers. Sweet Gale (Myrica Gale) with unopened brown catkins is the best of them all if procurable. Hornbeam, Beech or Whitethorn are good while quite bare, or with very young leafbuds. The bronze leaves of Prunus cerasifera Pissardii, or Amelanchier canadensis set with flower buds, provide a change as the season advances. Miss

15

Jekyll called attention to the effective use of leaves of the common wild Arum with large trumpet varieties in earthenware vessels.

I prefer Trumpets arranged in rather close bunches for effects of colour and mass, and the use of the smaller-flowered classes, Barrii, Leedsii, triandrus and so on, spaced irregularly among twigs in glass vases. I have never yet arranged a bowl of Daffodils that quite pleased me, nor admired any arranged by others. There seems something wrong about the angles at which the flowers radiate at the sides of a bowl.

A few flowers with sufficient leaves to represent the natural habit of growth can be arranged effectively in a bowl or an oriental bronze dish if held in place by strips of lead, but this seems to be a fussy and troublesome job, not so pleasing in the end as a bulb or two grown in a pot.

The Daffodils of Spring are the most welcome of all the flowers of the year for gathering. They come as the flowers of Iris unguicularis are on the wane, and beautiful as those are, they are so fugitive, lasting no more than two days in full beauty, that a flower with a long stem and some prospect of lasting for a full week comes as a pleasant change. Also we know that with the advent of Daffodils our outdoor gardens will provide us with constant supplies of flowers for cutting until November frosts destroy the latest Asters and we must look to Iris unguicularis once again.

Daffodils never make a braver show than when growing in grass, and so arranged that the grass may be seen as well as the Daffodils. Where they are planted evenly and thickly in wide stretches they too frequently suggest a crop instead of natural colonies, and an acre of crowded yellow blossoms resembles a field of Charlock or Mustard.

Nature's artistry may cause them to be thinned out in patches by an attack of Merodon and so produce a better effect, which could have been achieved by simpler means. It is impossible to lay down rules to suit all tastes and every type of grass-covered ground. Wide stretches of parkland, corners of lawns, fringes of meadows, edges of woodland and thin grass growing under trees require different treatment, but all are suitable for some kinds of Daffodils.

The first thing to think of is from what point of view the planting will be most often looked at. If it is to be seen chiefly from some distance, as would be the case in open parkland on either side of a main drive, bold massing would be necessary and large-flowered, tall varieties would probably prove most effective. If for grass verges of no great width between a drive and railed-off meadows, dwarf and small-flowered forms look well if planted so as to contrast here and there with taller kinds. The smaller varieties should be planted thinly for the most part, with a nucleus of closely planted bulbs somewhere in the drift to suggest mother-plants with stray seedlings stretching out from them, and generally only one variety should be used for such an effect. This may, however, be varied by mixing an early- and a late-flowering kind in a drift, taking care to place the nuclear masses apart, to look as though their seedlings had spread and mingled. Two kinds which flower together may be used mixed in equal number in the thinly planted portions. For this arrangement three crowded clumps should be planted, two of one variety close together and the third clump of the other variety placed farther from those than they are from one another, and anywhere in the drift so that it will not form a straight line with the two others.

The wild Lent Lily is one of the best for planting close to the eye, and can be mixed with Barrii conspicuus to give a later flowering that is yellow, or a poeticus variety for a change to white. Barrii and

poeticus ornatus generally flower sufficiently simultaneously to provide a good contrast. 'Ard Righ',
'Henry Irving' and obvallaris do well in grass in
some places, chiefly where well sheltered from wind,
and none are better for an early deep yellow effect.
The Leedsii forms 'Stella' and 'Stella superba',
'White Lady' and 'Evangeline' will come later and
turn your yellow drifts to white.

I find a good way to obtain a natural effect in a drift
is to choose the site for the nuclear group and lift the
grass with a spade, laying it aside to be replaced and
forking the ground into which the bulbs are to go.
Then place some white wooden labels at the limits
to which you wish that variety of Daffodil to stray.
Empty your bag or basketful of bulbs into the forked
patch, all of them in a heap, stoop down (or, better
still, kneel if the grass is fairly dry and your knees
are good but your clothes can only be said to have
been so once) and start by picking up a bulb or two
at a time and throwing them towards your labels.
Take rather poor aim so that many may fall short of
them and only a few reach the limiting target. Thus
you will thin down your heap to the number you think
the prepared patch should hold; plant those with a
trowel and replace the turf. If you have such a tool
as the thistle spud used on Sussex farms use it to lift
a tuft of turf wherever a scattered bulb has fallen
and push one in, stamping the turf down afterwards.

The outline of a drift that I like best is that of a
long fish, say a mackerel with one fork of its tail
omitted, but never make two neighbouring drifts the
same size or shape. It is a good plan to curve the
fish's back, bringing the head downwards and bending
the tail upwards. Drifts look best if arranged more or
less parallel with one another, but if it is intended that
they should be viewed from some special point, such
as a seat, the fishes' heads or tails can be pointed to-

wards it. In all cases avoid a uniformity of size and allowing the extremities of drifts to be in a straight line with those of their neighbours. After a little practice bulbs can be dropped on to the ground without the humiliating act of kneeling, and someone else can be set to plant them, but drop them yourself and watch the planting if you depute it to another.

For distant effects Trumpet varieties such as ' Emperor ', ' Empress ', ' Mme. de Graaff ' and other strong growers such as incomparabilis ' Sir Watkin ', Barrii conspicuus, poeticus ornatus and the fine old ' Pheasant's Eye ', latest of all to flower, are inexpensive and indestructible. Even though these may be planted in masses of as many thousands as land and purse permit, it is well to break the planting into drifts of varying lengths so that green turf may be seen winding between the plantings and at least one-third of grass to two of Daffodil blossoms. Then you may see Daffodils in a park or on a rough lawn, instead of the semblance of a bulb field where they are grown for market. Avoid double-flowered forms for planting in grass, even the old ' Van Sion ', early and richly golden though he be. His place is on the edge of a shrubbery in varying-sized clumps, some of which may wander in among deciduous shrubs; in grass he grows into coarse, thick tufts that look clumsy and are hard to get rid of. ' Princeps ', or N. Gayi as we should call it, was at one time much planted in grass, but should be avoided. It also forms clumps of too much thick leafage and seeds about too freely, producing mongrel offspring frequently of bad proportions and flimsy substance.

For corners of a lawn, or on either side of a grass path which leads to shrub borders, many choice small varieties can be trusted to settle down and be happy if the grass need not be mown before mid-June. A sunny, sheltered position should suit N. pallidiflorus,

which would race N. asturiensis to be the first to flower
in February, variiformis from the Pyrenees, ' Queen
of Spain ', the snow-white ' Undine ', Bulbocodium
varieties and cyclamineus, ' W. P. Milner ', and obvallaris. Any small choice kinds that have increased
freely in beds should be tried, and may be scattered
or planted in small clumps according to the taste of
their owner. If they prove a success pray plant the
lovely Crocus nudiflorus, so plentiful in Pyrenean turf,
to flower in October and play at Box and Cox with
the Narcissi.

If planted in meadows Daffodils should be confined
to one side only and planted in groups of three to five
bulbs, spaced at least a yard apart to allow cattle
to graze between them, and these groups should be
for the most part collected into colonies of one kind,
and only mingling with those of another form or
colour where a constellation of one variety joins another
distinct one. It helps to create a natural effect if
one variety, such as Barrii conspicuus, is represented
by an occasional crowded clump or two in each of the
other constellations, as well as having one or two in
its own. Be careful here also to leave intervening
spaces of unplanted turf of irregular shape and size.
N. biflorus and ' Pheasant's Eye ' are good for planting
in meadows. N. pallidiflorus, like Snowdrops, is
sometimes quite happy and seeds freely in thin turf
among tree roots.

So long as varieties are not mixed haphazard like
the ingredients of a cake, to be dotted singly at even
distances in turf, the greatest pleasure of the Daffodil
season will be the effects of late-evening sunlight on
those well established in grass.

The leaves of Daffodils, though never eaten by cattle
while still green, are not injurious when dried in hay.
In the Scilly Isles stacks are made of nothing but
Narcissus leaves and stalks, and I have seen cattle that

will prefer a bundle of such hay to one of Clover if both are offered to them at the same time.

I find it hard to decide whether it is my duty to advise the ordinary garden-lover to raise seedling Daffodils or to warn him so strongly as to the difficulties and labour involved that he may rest contented to leave it alone and avail himself of the successes gained by others. It will be only fair to state a few facts on both sides.

In favour of raising seedlings there is Mr. Burbidge's advice: 'Raise seedlings, hybrids if you can, but raise seedlings.' Then there is certainly such a thing as ' Beginner's Luck '; or at any rate we have heard instances of it. It may be a parallel with the coming true of dreams in which hits are counted, misses forgotten.

One of the most thrilling of garden experiences is to look over a bed of seedlings flowering for the first time. It carries with it the danger of parental pride and a tendency to promote what to others would be obvious geese to the imaginary rank of swans.

It certainly encourages the virtue of Patience, a waiting period of four to five years being usual between sowing and flowering; and again it has an educational value: the processes of fertilisation, germination and the development of bulbs are worth observing and understanding.

On the other hand, to produce strong, healthy flowering bulbs means the provision of much good soil, a cold frame for two seasons, a choice position in the garden after that, and the spending of a good deal of time and labour.

There will be a large proportion of worthless forms, difficult to dispose of unless your heart is hard enough to permit of their cremation. Even after the first flowering several years must pass before the constitution, and freedom of flowering and increase, have been sufficiently tested to warrant the growing on of your favourite selections; and pray do not name and register any before they have stood those tests satisfactorily and are really better than some known variety of similar appearance.

After ten years of hope and mild admiration for a long bed of home-raised seedlings, we have decided to offer them for sale at a penny each for mother-bulbs and two a penny for rounds, on the flower stall of the Parish Fête, hoping to be easily rid of them and to benefit the Parish Fund simultaneously. Therefore may I remind you of Mr. Punch's advice to those about to marry ? It was ' Don't '.

If you cannot resist the temptation to hybridise, read carefully the chapters thereon in Bourne's *Book of the Daffodil* and in Jacob's *Daffodils*. In case you have not access to those, read the following instructions.

For cross-pollinating you need a pair of finely pointed forceps. The flower selected as seed parent should be chosen when freshly opened and its anthers removed by the forceps before its pollen is dusty. Flowers prepared thus should be protected from insect visitors by glass or fine muslin, but it is safer to grow the mother-plants in pots in a greenhouse.

When the stigma is seen to be open and looking moist it is ready to receive pollen. An anther from the other parent should be removed by the forceps and held in them so that the pollen may be gently smeared on to the stigma, and all should be well.

The pollinated plant should then be marked by a number, and that number and the cross it represents should be entered in a notebook.

Seeds should be gathered before the pods burst, generally when they show any trace of turning yellow. They should be sown as soon as possible after gathering, thinly in drills, in boxes or pans, or better still in a cold-frame itself. The soil should be of the best, a mixture of loam and plenty of sharp sand. If boxes are used, they should be deeper than the ordinary kinds, to allow of the young plants pulling themselves down for at least 3 inches if they want to. Except in mild climates, where seeds should be sown in the open ground, boxes or pans must be stood in a frame. The seedlings should be kept in the boxes for two seasons, then turned out when dormant in July and the bulbs planted in rows in prepared beds, where they should be left until they flower.

XXI

PESTS AND DISEASES

IT IS sad that a chapter with so disagreeable a heading must be included, and more depressing still that with our present knowledge there can be no triumphant proclamation at its close that a perfect mastery over the enemies of the Daffodil has been reached.

With all the experience gained in years of research we can hardly hold our own against insects, fungi and what are suspected to be virus diseases, which attack the Narcissus. In fact, almost every season adds the name of some fresh horror to the list.

It was said of old that the gods rejoiced to see a good man struggling against adversity. Let us hope that the goodness of Daffodil growers may be increased by each fresh combat with eelworm, fly or stripe.

It is unfortunately only a natural consequence that when men greatly increase the area of cultivation of any plant, and select strains for characters other than resistance to disease, the field is widened for the spread of pests and diseases hitherto held in check by the lack of opportunity for rapid increase.

Thus many hitherto negligible native disorders have suddenly become agents of wholesale destruction; and the introduction of plants from other countries has frequently been accompanied by some disease or destructive insect.

So it has been with the Large Narcissus-fly, *Merodon equestris*, a native of Southern Europe, which was first definitely recorded in England in 1865, but is now only too plentiful in most countries where Narcissi are cultivated in quantity.

234

It will attack most of the bulbous plants of the
Order Amaryllideae as well as Narcissus. It is especially
disastrous to Snowdrops. One Narcissus bulb is
generally sufficient for the full growth of a Merodon,
but it must devour three or more Snowdrop bulbs
before it is fully fed. Habranthus pratensis is a
favourite food and needs special protection where
this fly is plentiful. It has also been found in some
Liliaceous plants, Scilla nutans, Hyacinth and Galtonia
among them.

Merodon and other pests have been ably and fully
dealt with in Bulletin No. 51 issued by the Ministry
of Agriculture, which should be studied by all who are
interested in Daffodils. However, some short notes
on pests may be usefully included here.

It is most important to learn to recognise the Narcissus-fly when on the wing. It is about the size of
an ordinary bluebottle, but has a black body covered
with hair, so that it looks more like a small bumble-bee
than a fly. The hairs vary in colour in different individuals. In some they form bands of grey or orange
on the thorax and the abdomen, or on one of these only.
In aged specimens the hair may be worn off the thorax,
which is then black and shining.

If one is caught in a butterfly net and examined
closely it will be seen that it is a true fly, a dipteron, possessing only one wing on each side of its thorax, whereas
all hymenopterous insects, to which order bees and wasps
belong, have four wings, a large and a smaller one on
each side. Again the antennæ of bees are very noticeable, but the large eyes of Merodon have no jointed,
long antennæ (feelers, as people often call them) on
either side, but two short apologies for them, sprouting
out from the central front of the head.

Their abominable habit is to appear on the wing
in the hottest and sunniest part of the day from mid-
May till July, just at the very time that many pleasanter

gardening jobs are to be found than hunting flies in the hot sunshine. Small boys soon learn to recognise them and will hunt them eagerly with butterfly nets for the sake of a penny a fly. A hundred or two fly corpses are well worth the needful expenditure.

The females lay their eggs among the bases of leaves, or in cavities in the soil near the neck of a bulb. They possess an ovipositor that can be extended for about $\frac{1}{4}$ inch, which must be very serviceable for placing the egg safely out of sight. The young larva travels down the outside of a bulb and bores a small hole through the side of the basal root-plate, from which it eats its way into the heart of the bulb, making a most disgusting mess on its way. Sometimes one will bore a second and larger hole through the base of the bulb to serve as a drain, and these half-devoured bulbs are easily detected but unless very precious are seldom worth saving from the bonfire, as wounded bulbs favour infection by eelworm.

A little practice should enable anyone to detect the presence of a young Merodon grub in a bulb at lifting time. If a small rust-coloured wound is noticed on the basal plate it should be investigated with the aid of a sharp penknife. A little scratching and scooping will generally reveal a small tunnel, and probing with a long pin, bent into a small hook at its point, often ends in the extraction of the enemy and the salvation of a valuable bulb. The Hot-Water Treatment, as used against eelworm, is also useful for destroying Merodon grubs. One hour's immersion in water heated to 110° F. will kill them. I have been able to drown out larvæ from Habranthus and Narcissus bulbs placed in a pail of cold water and left to soak for two days, having previously widened the entrance tunnels.

Spraying with Arsenic and Glycerine has been tried for killing the adult flies in large bulb fields. It is too elaborate an undertaking for the ordinary garden, and liable to kill bees.

Two lesser flies of the genus *Eumerus* attack bulbs, and as they produce two or more broods in the year can do a great deal of damage. I encourage a personal belief (or is it only a hope?) that they mostly attack bulbs that are exposed to the air when stored in sheds or laid on the ground during lifting. However, it has been established that the females can reach bulbs in the ground by going down the cavities left by dead foliage. Raking over of ground after the removal of foliage may help to prevent this.

Eumerus lays many eggs on one bulb, and the larvæ make such a terrible mess of it that it rapidly becomes a soft mass of decayed matter. Bulbs should never be laid out in the open or stored where Eumerus flies can gain access to them.

The flies resemble small Hover-flies in appearance, and being only about ¼ inch in length are not easily noticed unless present in unpleasantly large numbers.

Besides the damage done by Narcissus-flies in their ordinary evil habits of feeding upon our bulbs, they unconsciously aid and abet other pernicious rascals to do the same. Bulb Mites are active at the same period as Narcissus-flies, and contrive to cling on to them and to be carried from place to place. Bulb Mites mostly attack damaged bulbs, and there is no doubt that their presence prevents slightly injured bulbs from recovering.

I believe that Naphthalene crystals scattered among the Narcissus foliage in late May acts as a deterrent to egg-laying by the flies, and it is not harmful to the bulbs, and one of the cheapest and easiest methods to employ.

The most deadly enemy is the microscopic Nematode, the Bulb Eelworm, *Tylenchus* or *Anguillulina dipsaci*, for if unchecked it is capable of destroying a whole collection of Narcissi.

Its ravages became so serious that the Royal Horticultural Society undertook an investigation into its cause and prevention at their Research Station at Wisley, which established the identity of the parasitic worm and the possibility of killing it by what is now known as the Hot-Water Treatment.

Careful experiments showed that if dormant bulbs are placed in hot water to be maintained at a temperature of 110° F. for three hours, the heat proves fatal to the eelworm, and the bulbs are not seriously injured, but for the most part are stimulated to more rapid increase and vigorous growth, though, if not treated at the proper time (which varies with different varieties), the flowers may be affected and become ragged and distorted in the following season.

Excellent forms of apparatus for the sterilisation of bulbs are now procurable, ranging from small portable patterns suitable for an amateur's garden to huge affairs which will cook a ton of bulbs at a time.

Whenever the presence of eelworm is suspected a few samples of bulbs should be examined. If cut through across the lower portion of the neck, the trouble may be recognised by the white bulb-scales showing dark brown, decayed material between their layers. For further confirmation a little of this brown matter should be extracted, laid on a glass slide and a drop of water added to it. A microscope is necessary, as the worms are too small to be seen by the naked eye or through an ordinary pocket lens. Full-grown specimens are only $\frac{1}{20}$ inch long, and they are colourless and transparent. Under the microscope, however, they can be plainly seen swarming out from the decayed matter and wriggling about in the water.

The presence of eelworms in dormant bulbs while in store should be suspected if upon gentle pressure between the fingers they feel softer than others, and a few such bulbs should be cut open and examined. When growing, dwarfed and contorted growths, or the presence on the leaves of irregular blotches resembling blisters of yellowish colouring, known as ' spickles ', are almost certain indications of eelworm in the bulb.

All badly infected bulbs should be removed and they, and the soil in which they grew, should be burnt. At the next lifting all neighbouring bulbs should be sterilised and planted in fresh ground. One of the worst troubles connected with an attack of eelworm is the length of time that must elapse before the ground can be regarded as free from infection. This may be for three or more seasons, and is a serious matter for people with limited space. No Onions, Scillas or other bulbous plant should be grown on infected ground, and certain weeds, especially plantains, are capable of supporting generations of eelworm. Unfortunately no satisfactory method of treating soil so as to render it innocuous has yet been discovered.

The Board of Agriculture's leaflet on *Fusarium bulbigenum*, one of the many diseases due to fungi which attack Narcissi, should be obtained by all who notice small yellowish spots on the leaves of their Daffodils. It is not a very cheering publication, as it offers no quick and easy curative treatment.

Mosaic or Grey Disease has been studied here and in Holland and America, but beyond regarding it as a form of virus, possibly spread by punctures made by minute insects, and as being ultramicroscopic and therefore invisible except in its effects, no definitely helpful pronouncement has been made.

The presence of Mosaic is declared by the striping or mottling of leaves, the markings generally consisting of yellow lines or patches among the normal blue-green of the leaf. Plants affected by it are greatly weakened, causing the deterioration of the stock, and it is safest to destroy them as soon as the disease is discovered.

Sometimes leaves are affected in the season following Hot-Water Treatment, and show various degrees of striping, which is usually confined to the upper portion of the leaves, but sometimes takes the form of bands across them. It should not be accompanied by any lack of vigour and may be ignored.

Another fungus, possibly of the genus Fusarium, attacks the root-plate and the bases of outer bulb-scales, causing what is known as Basal Rot. Once there the decay spreads into the inside of the bulb, especially while in store, and is aggravated by a warm temperature of about 70° to 90° F. This disease is much more prevalent in wet soils than in well-drained ones, and frequently disappears when bulbs affected with Basal Rot are transferred to well-drained ground.

The decayed portion does not become slimy or damp, but rather dry and spongy, and the mycelium of the fungus may break through the surface and produce a patch of whitish mould where the scales join the root-plate. The form of Fusarium that attacks the Narcissus is not known to affect other bulbous plants. The large Trumpets and certain poeticus varieties are the most susceptible; Poetaz varieties and Jonquils are the most resistant. All affected bulbs should be sorted out and burnt before any undergo Hot-Water Treatment, which, without the addition of a disinfectant, might spread the disease. Uspulum has been recommended for this purpose, but its efficacy is still in question.

More than one form of black scale-speck fungus can be occasionally found on the scales of bulbs. Their effect on healthy bulbs is still in doubt. One kind forms flat, black specks about the size of the head of a pin on the outer scales. These specks are the

resting bodies of the fungus, and no great harm to
bulbs has been caused by them. Another produces
smaller specks and may have some affinity with the
Sclerotium that attacks Gladiolus and Freesia bulbs,
and may prove more dangerous than the last.

The wintering bodies of *Stagonospora Curtisii*, or
Leaf-scorch fungus, may also be found on the dead
ends of scales in the necks of bulbs. In this disease
the tips of leaves appear blighted, as though by frost,
when they first emerge. From these dead portions
the reproductive bodies of the fungus burst out, and
spores are distributed by rain to other plants, causing
further mischief and the early dying off of the foliage.
Affected bulbs should be disinfected in Formaldehyde,
and growing leaves sprayed with Bordeaux Mixture.
One part of Saponin to 8,000 of mixture (i.e. 1 ounce to
50 gallons) must be added to make the spray adhere to
the leaves.

Ramularia-blight is caused by the fungus *R. valli-
sumbrosae*, and can be recognised by brown leaf-tips
which differ from those caused by Stagonospora by
producing quantities of white spores. These also
occur on the green portion of the leaf, sometimes in
such quantities that clouds of them settle on those
walking through an infected planting and whiten their
clothing. This blight was first noticed in Italy by
Cavara in 1889. He found it in the Botanical Garden
at Vallombrosa, hence its specific name. It is most
troublesome in places with a damp atmosphere and
heavy rainfall, where it will infest the soil. Spraying
with Bordeaux Mixture, rotation of crops and disin-
fection of bulbs are the best preventive measures.

The Bulb-Scale Mite, *Tarsonemus approximatus* var.
Narcissi, has lately appeared in England, chiefly among
forced bulbs. It is believed that it cannot stand
temperatures so low as occur in normal winters in this
country, and thus will be confined to plants grown

16

under glass. The mites feed between the fleshy bulb-scales, and the standard Hot-Water Treatment is sufficient to destroy them.

Let us hope that there will be no fresh addition to the list of pests before this appears in print—or after.

INDEX